A COMPLETE GUIDE TO
DEMOLITION

A COMPLETE GUIDE TO

DEMOLITION

David M Pledger

THE CONSTRUCTION PRESS LTD

D

624.1

PLE

ISBN 0 904406 22 9
Copyright 1977 © David M. Pledger

Published in 1977 by:

The Construction Press Ltd.,
Lunesdale House,
Hornby,
Lancaster, LA2 8NB

Contents

Preface

This book has been written as it was felt by both the author and the publishers that the separation of the various disciplines of the Building Team into distinct professions has meant that some of the processes involved in building have been left too long almost to chance. The demolition of buildings on site has so often been virtually an afterthought which has had to be squeezed between acquisition and vacation and the commencement of work by the Main Contractor, and carried out as quickly and cheaply as possible. This has worked in the past without too many problems so long as the buildings being demolished were simple structures, as they could be pulled down and the cleared site levelled off by a few men with comparatively unsophisticated equipment.

The much wider use of both reinforced and mass concrete, industrialized building techniques, and high rise buildings are now all beginning to impinge upon the demolition contractor's work. In addition to the problems these new techniques are bringing, the what might be deemed traditional nuisances of demolition, the production of dust, noise, fires and general blighting of areas awaiting redevelopment, are becoming more and more undesirable, obtrusive, and anti-social, though sites are tending to be smaller and more restricted.

The dangers presented by the new building techniques to demolition workers, the public, and the ecology, are beginning to increase; there are pre-stressed and post-tensioned beams, steel-framed buildings, and industrialized buildings, on the demolition of which very little practical experience has been gained, and allied to these there are the new materials, which may be dangerous to demolish especially in view of the fact that the details both of the construction of any building and of any changes which may have been made to it during its lifetime can so easily be forgotten. There are, for example, volatile fuel storage tanks, asbestos pipe laggings, abandoned chemicals, and inflammable foam infills, and we cannot yet know what else there may be in the future.

At the present time, there is no legal requirement for minutely detailed plans of buildings to be kept so it is very difficult to obtain the construction data of any building, even if of very recent origin. It has been suggested by the Vice-President of the National Federation of Demolition Contractors that a designer should be made to file his specifications not only for the construction of a building, but also for its demolition, preferably with the records department of some central authority. Even if this is not feasible — and certainly it does not seem likely that there will be any compulsory move in this direction in the near future — responsible bodies should pay more attention to demolition requirements, and particularly to the time required to carry out the job, in order that more pre-specification research may be made and that the work may be planned not only with more efficient use of plant and men, but also with a view to causing as little environmental damage as possible.

High Ongar, Essex.

David M. Pledger

ACKNOWLEDGEMENTS

The author wishes to thank:—

1) Dr. V. Powell-Smith, LLB. (Hons), LL.M., D.Litt., F.F.B., Secretary of the National Federation of Demolition Contractors, for providing the introduction relating to the organisation of the industry.

2) M. W. Pullin, B.Sc., M.Inst.P., M.R.S.H. and P. E. Forrester, M.R.S.H. of the Greater London Council, the Scientific Adviser to the Greater London Council, and the Royal Society of Health for granting permission to publish Appendix 4.

3) The Directors, staff and operatives of Yates Associated Demolition Ltd.

4) The Directors, staff and operatives of Tulkon Demolition and Construction Ltd.

5) His colleagues and friends in the Borough Architect's Department of the London Borough of Haringey and all those people who provided photographs and shared their knowledge and experience.

Above: Typical examples of ill-managed and well organised demolition sites.

Introduction

The Demolition Industry Today

Dr. V. Powell-Smith, LL.B. (Hons), LL.M., D.Litt., F.F.B.
Secretary of the National Federation of Demolition Contractors

It is estimated that there are approximately 6,000 demolition operatives in the United Kingdom*, but it is impossible to estimate with any degree of accuracy the number of demolition firms operating in the same area. This is because new firms are established almost every day, and many of them are of a short-lived nature.

The National Federation of Demolition Contractors Limited has about 180 subscribing members, and this figure has remained more or less constant since 1971. The Federation takes the view that it represents approximately two-thirds of *bona fide* employers who are engaged wholly or mainly in demolition work. If this figure is accurate, it means that there are approximately 270 *bona fide* demolition contractors in the United Kingdom. To this number there must be added those members of the British Scrap Federation who undertake works of dismantling, which is akin to demolition. These probably amount to about 100 firms and limited companies. This gives us an approximate figure of 370 organisations engaged wholly or mainly in demolition and dismantling in Great Britain. Outside this main stream, there are many hundreds of fringe operators.

Works of demolition and dismantling are carried out by four major types of business organisation, namely:

a) general demolition contractors;

b) dismantling contractors, who are associated with the scrap metal business;

c) specialist sub-contractors such as explosives engineers;

d) civil engineering contractors.

In addition, many general builders undertake demolition work from time to time, but usually only on a very small scale.

This division is not of any great significance, except possibly in the field of labour relations, where different working rules may apply. Indeed, this is recognised by the recently-formed Demolition and Dismantling Industry Register, membership of which requires observance of a number of basic criteria including the "appropriate working rule agreement"

Firms engaged in demolition and dismantling range in size from sole

---

* By the Department of Employment in its statistical survey.

traders to limited companies employing 120 operatives or more. The sole traders are, more often than not, specialists in particular techniques, such as the controlled application of explosives.

It should also be appreciated that a number of contractors have particular specialisms, an unusual one being that of concentrating largely on the demolition of worked-out collieries.

The Demolition Industry Conciliation Board, which is the official wage-negotiating body for the industry, classifies the operatives employed according to their respective skills. The principal classifications (apart from mechanical plant operators) are:

a) general labourers, who work largely at ground level,

b) mattockmen, who work at intermediate height,

c) topmen, who are the 'craftsmen' of the industry, capable of working safely at any height.

These are very broad classifications and, in fact, there are very few mattockmen as such. Operatives are mainly either general labourers or topmen but there are a number of intermediate skills such as timber shorers and burners, i.e. operatives skilled in the use of burning equipment. Mechanical plant operators are also extremely important to the industry, but most demolition contractors regard the topman as the most important skilled operative.

There is virtually no relationship between the size of the demolition business and the type of organization used for conducting it. The majority of members of the National Federation of Demolition Contractors and of the British Scrap Federation are constituted as limited liability companies. Amongst these private companies there is a wide variation in the scale of operations from that of the concern with two or three employees and a nominal capital of £100 to very substantial concerns with a turnover in excess of half a million pounds sterling.

The demolition contractor's preference for the advantages of limited liability contrasts sharply with the reluctance of builders to adopt that form of organisation for their businesses. One commentator* dealing with this matter estimated that "taking the country as a whole 25 per cent of all businesses in the constructional industry are registered as companies according to the geographical region and the nature of the work". No such variation is apparent in the membership of the National Federation of Demolition Contractors.

Much of the labour employed by demolition contractors is peripatetic; indeed, one of the major problems besetting the industry is that of casual labour. Reputable contractors do not like to rely on this sort of labour but, in many areas, they are forced to employ it. Because of the inherently dangerous nature of the work, and the fact that even the general labourer in demolition requires certain skills, the practice is not the same as in the building industry at large. The casual labour in demolition is formed by a pool of men who, apparently, migrate around a particular geographical area. Whereas in the construction industry it is not uncommon to find that students are employed as general labourers during academic vacations, this is virtually unknown in the demolition industry.

---

* See J.R. Colclough, "The Construction Industry of Great Britain", 1965, p. 22.

Another possible classification of demolition contractors is according to the work they undertake. Over ninety-nine per cent of the members of the National Federation of Demolition Contractors will undertake "general demolition" and about ninety-five per cent will undertake site clearance and excavation. When we come to consider the more specialised forms of demolition — such as chimney demolition and that of mass and reinforced concrete foundations — the percentage drops to eighty and seventy-six per cent respectively*.

Most demolition contractors work in defined geographical regions, though some seventy-five per cent of the membership of the National Federation of Demolition Contractors expresses its willingness to work anywhere in Great Britain. It seems, however, that only the largest contractors, e.g. those employing 50 or more demolition operatives, do undertake work on a nation wide scale.

*National Federation of Demolition Contractors, "Demolition 1972/73", pp. 8-9.

Part 1

Demolition and the Architect

1.1 The Preliminary Survey

As already stated, the object of this book is to provide a guide to all aspects of demolition, and there are numerous factors, several not immediately apparent, which must be taken into account before the actual method of demolition can be decided upon, and which may need inclusion in and may affect the specification being prepared. A check list with the more frequent points is given in Appendix 1. However, the following factors should be considered at this stage as they may affect later decisions.

The age and condition of the structure

The age, method of construction, and condition of the building will all have a great influence on the Contractor's choice of demolition method, on his decision as to what items should be retained, and of course on the likely cost of the work. A survey should be made of the property, and the Architect should consider whether special mention should be made of any restrictions which will affect the cost of the tender.

THE SURROUNDING SITE

Trees

The damage that is sustained in many cases by mature trees which the Architect may have wished to retain as part of the new scheme is one of the most common causes of bad feeling between the Demolition Contractor and the Architect, and it is at this early stage that instructions must be given that any trees which are not to be removed from the site must be adequately protected by the Contractor and not just retained. Damage is most commonly caused either through the trees being scorched by fires lit on the site (indeed for some reason demolition operatives are strongly attracted to the practice of heaping bonfires up against trees), or through their being hit by lorries or machines.

Trees and shrubs which are to be retained should be listed, numbered on drawings, and described in the Contract Documents. A fence or protective screen should be erected at a minimum distance of say 1.3 metres (4') from the bole of the tree, and a watch kept throughout the duration of the building operations so that any damage to bark on trunk or branches can be tidied up and painted over with a bitumen compound as soon as possible.

Existing boundary fences

It is usual, after a long period of time, for separating fences between gardens and parcels of land to be allowed to deteriorate, often completely beyond repair.

It is an excellent idea to arrange for photographs to be taken of existing fences prior to demolition and site clearance, in order to provide evidence in cases where boundary fences are alleged to have been damaged. Experience has shown that in most cases it is inadvisable to use any existing brick boundary walls as site boundaries unless it is certain that they will be well protected. Vandals and children seem to delight in breaking away sections of brickwork — which is very simple to do when the bricks have been laid in lime mortar, as they were in so many old walls — and any wall so damaged very quickly becomes dangerous to everybody in the vicinity.

Public services

The exact location must be found of all services on the site and whenever possible these should all be plotted on a site plan. Those which are not to be used by the new buildings will have to be cut off, plugged, or diverted at the boundary of the site (see next chapter), and financial provision for doing this will have to be made in the Contract Documents. Any cables, drains, service pipes or ducts which cross the site should be marked and protected from damage by impact, heavy loads, or interference. Branch drains which are not to be connected for use should be sealed off as close to the main sewer as possible, and the disused branch filled with pulverized fuel ash (P.F.A.) or cement/sand slurry as soon as possible. It is regretted that in many cases this operation is not carried out, and this fact has no doubt contributed in no small way to the increase there has been in rat infestation in urban areas in recent years.

The services described above may include:—

1. drainage
2. electricity supply cables
3. gas pipework
4. water supply pipes
5. post office telephone cables
6. radio and television relay lines
7. hydraulic pressure mains
8. district heating mains.

Rights of way

Legal documents and Ordnance Survey maps must be studied to see whether there is any recorded right of way across the land to be developed. Also any sign that any person has been using an unrecorded right of way across the property for any length of time should be noted and brought to the attention of the site owner's legal advisers.

THE BUILDINGS TO BE DEMOLISHED

As already stated, the age and condition of the building to be demolished is of prime importance. The age and condition of the immediately surrounding property should similarly be taken into account. Adjacent properties might, for example, be relying for support on the property to be demolished. In this case any Party Wall Awards will have to be checked, and the statutory and legal responsibilities towards the other party will have to be considered. These matters will be covered in Chapter 1.4 where the principles of weather-proofing, shoring and support works will be discussed.

Since the last decades of the nineteenth century, anyone carrying out building works has been required to deposit plans of the proposed structure with the Local Council, and if possible copies of these should be studied, but it should be remembered that alterations may have been carried out to boundaries and drainage, especially in the case of older buildings.

In this first survey the proposed method of demolition should be considered in a very general sense only, in order that some guidance can be obtained as to any likely restrictions and these can be allowed for in the specification. In particular, the following points should be investigated.

The type of ground on which the structure is erected

This matter is one that at first sight may seem to be irrelevant, but it may affect the future work. Some soils, particularly clay, can transmit shock waves for a considerable distance, and structural damage could be caused to surrounding properties if a large section or member of the structure were felled. If,therefore,considerable impact shock or vibration could result from the work, special attention should be paid to the insurance provisions in this respect, and it may be advantageous to arrange for schedules of conditions to be agreed upon with owners of nearby properties.

Items which can be salvaged and retained for use

Depending upon the future use of the building, there may be items which could be retained and preserved either for incorporation in the new structure or perhaps for display. Most of these are immediately obvious, but it is surprising how much decorative miscellanea is destroyed when a little thought might have found a use for it. A list of possible items for salvage follows, but this can only be very general in scope.

a) Roofs — decorated terra cotta finials and chimney pots, handmade tiles, decorated hopper heads on rainwater goods.

b) Walls — lintels and enrichments, Insurance Company plates.

c) Windows and doors — stained glass, brassware.

d) External items — wrought or cast iron railings, York stone paving.

In addition, a wealth of timber mouldings, plasterwork, tiles and other materials is often to be found,especially on houses dating from the late Victorian period.

Basements, cellars, etc.

A careful survey should be made of any basements, cellars or underground storage tanks in the property to be demolished, and, if possible, in the adjoining properties too.

In many Victorian Houses the coal cellar extended under the public pavement, and there was an access manhole in this for delivery of supplies. If any such manholes are found the Highway Authority in the area will have to be consulted; shuttering is then usually placed and the void under the pavement filled with a lean concrete, a 1:10 mix being adequate. The cost of this work will have to be included in the contract.

At this stage consideration should be given to the future use of the area where the basement is situated. There is a temptation, if this is outside the area of the new foundations, for the property owner to instruct the Demolition Contractor to fill the void with hardcore or surplus earth, but it is recommended that this practice be avoided and the Demolition Contractor be instructed to leave the basement area empty of all rubbish, but of course securely fenced. This will enable a proper survey of the basement area to be made later, and the subsequent breaking up of the basement floor and filling with hardcore or surplus soil can take place when the Main Building Contractor is on site, and, it is hoped, more control can be imposed over the quality of the fill.

If, therefore, it is decided that the basement should be kept empty for a period, it should not be forgotten that any cross-walls should only be removed if there is no possibility of external forces pushing the walls of the basement inwards when the stabilizing load from the superstructure has been removed.

Partial demolition

Whilst it is not envisaged that a detailed plan for the actual demolition be formulated at this stage, the Architect should bear in mind the following basic facts which may be especially important when partial demolition of a building, e.g. for alterations etc., is envisaged.

a) Attention should be paid to the structural design of the building, in order to determine which parts of the structure depend upon each other to maintain structural stability.

b) Some building frames may rely on infill wall panels for stability in one or more directions, and the indiscriminate removal of panels may seriously impair the stability of the structure.

c) The erection of structural steel-work frequently involves the pulling of members into position before the final welding, bolting, or rivetting of connections. This sets up forces which, together with the effects of movement during settlement, can cause considerable springing of the frame during demolition, with the attendant dangers of accident or damage.

d) Many balconies, canopies, and staircases are of cantilevered construction, and considerable danger may ensue once the weight of the structure above has been removed.

e) Very little practical experience has been obtained up to now in the demolition of pre-stressed and post-tensioned concrete structural members, and it is necessary at the outset to ascertain the system of stressing and construction that was used. Any cutting or breaking away of concrete for site inspection should only be done at points selected by a Chartered Engineer experienced in this type of construction.

Wells, and underground storage tanks

The position, depth, and type of any wells should be noted, and if necessary arrangements made for these to be adequately sealed or fenced.

The most frequently found underground storage tanks are those which have been used for petroleum or diesel fuel. These should have been emptied of fuel and filled with water when the building was vacated, and because of the dangers of explosion and fire a check should be made at survey stage that this has been done. The actual removal of the tanks is discussed in a later chapter, but it should be noted at this point that the Local Authority Petroleum Officer has to be informed, and his guidance must be followed when the time comes for removal and disposal of the tanks.

Previous uses of building and sites

Enquiries should be made to determine, if possible, the uses to which the buildings to be demolished have been put. There are many processes which produce dangerous wastes, and dangers may arise from volatile liquids, inflammable or explosive materials, and injurious chemical or radio-active materials, all of which have been left on sites in the past.

Ordnance Survey benchmarks

The structure should be examined for any sign of a benchmark. These are Ordnance Survey markings, usually in one of two forms:

a) A brass plate about 7 ins x 4 ins (177.8 mm x 101.6 mm) inscribed:—

O.S.

B.M.

b) A broad arrow, with a bar above chisel cut into brickwork or masonry.

If either form exists on the structure to be demolished (they are also shown on the Ordnance 1/500 and 1/1250 sheets), the local Ordnance Survey Office must be informed.

Lightning conductors

In some older types of lightning conductors a milli curie source of radium was fitted to the top. Radium has a half life of 1620 years, so old conductors might well be radio active.

Street closures or diversions

If a diversion or temporary closure of pedestrian footways or traffic routes is likely to be necessary, then arrangements will have to be made with the Local Authority. It is as well to do this at this stage as there can sometimes be lengthy delays in these matters.

Noise, dust, and other nuisances

The most common complaints about demolition works from members of the public and occupants of surrounding buildings regard fires on site, dust, and noise, probably in that order. Unless the client is prepared to pay considerably to have rubbish and timber carted away from the demolition works, there will obviously have to be burning on site. The Architect should note anything that might be damaged by careless burning and warn the Demolition Contractor if necessary. (See Chapter 1.2 for details of Insurance requirements and Contract Clauses relating to this.

The amount of dust raised both by the pulling-down process and the loading of hardcore can be considerable, and can create a particular problem in enclosed sites. A temporary water supply should be specified, and the rubbish should be sprayed throughout the work if necessary.

If the site is enclosed, or the Contractor intends to use compressors or concrete breakers, a note should be made of the possibility that working hours may have to be restricted, for future inclusion in the Specification of Works.

Hoardings and scaffolding

Finally, to complete the "Pre Specification" Survey, a note should be made of what hoardings, fans and protective scaffoldings will need to be specified for the duration of the demolition works. It should also be noted whether it will be necessary for any of these to remain throughout the Building Contract period, and whether the Demolition Contractor will be required to return afterwards to dismantle them and remove them from the site.

1.2 The Contract

CHOICE OF CONTRACTOR

The selection of the Demolition Contractor may be made by one of various well-tried methods:—

a) Prospective tenderers can be advertised for in trade and local journals.

b) A list of tenderers whose performance and references are known to be satisfactory can be kept by the Architect and a selected number of these invited to quote in competition.

c) A tender figure and specification can be negotiated with a firm whose abilities are known to the Architect.

Which method is chosen will depend on the volume of work controlled by the Architect and the complexity and urgency of the proposed project.

The main disadvantage of method a) is that it may well be that applications will be received from many contractors who are totally unsuited to the project, and considerable time and effort may have to be wasted in selection. The main disadvantage of method c) is that the cost quoted may well depend more on the Contractor's work load at the time of quoting than on the true cost of the work.

As a general rule, therefore, method b) is favoured in most cases, and this does enable the Employer (whether he is an Architect or an Engineer acting as an agent) to restrict the production of Contract Documents to a reasonable number, and there is some advantage in having at least the implied threat of removal from the approved list if the work falls below a required standard.

Regardless of whatever method is used for selection of tenders, a formal contract in writing should be prepared and it should be signed by the building owner (or his representative) and the Demolition Contractor.

The general form of contract is perhaps beyond the scope of this book but it can usually be based on the Standard Form of Contract compiled by the Royal Institute of British Architects, the contract compiled by the Institute of Civil Engineers, or of course the standard form of the National Federation of Demolition Contractors. These contracts cover general terms and conditions, and most local authorities and Government Bodies have their own versions. A sample set of conditions of contract and tender form appears in Appendix 2.

SPECIAL CONTRACT REQUIREMENTS

In addition to the general requirements set out in the contract form and the items in the Specification of Works which will need adapting to suit specific cases, there are a few other requirements which deserve special attention and careful thought.

Insurance
(see Appendix 2 for standard clause)

The importance of this item cannot be over-emphasised and the Architect should insist on being shown up-to-date renewal receipts in addition to the policy itself.

The Demolition Contractor should be fully insured with a reputable company against all actions, costs, demands, and expenses, in respect of any accident or injury to any of his workmen, or any third party, or any loss or damage to property, including roads and services. The cover in respect of the following should be checked in the light of the size and location of the project:—

a) collapse, subsidence, vibration, and/or weakening of support,

b) use of various types of plant or cranes,

c) injuries to third parties,

d) claims in respect of consequential damage,

e) fires and burning on site.

It will be noted that most conditions of contract do not hold the Contractor responsible for any claims arising from act, neglect, or omission by the Employer or his servants.

Guarantee bond or deposit

In cases where the property to be demolished contains a reasonable amount of salvageable materials a credit may be expected to be payable by the Contractor to the Employer. This payment should be made *before* any work is allowed to commence on the site. If, as is more likely today, there is a substantial amount of salvageable material but not enough to produce a credit balance, the Architect should estimate what might reasonably be expected to be removed from the building and require that a bond for that value be entered into or deposited with him at an agreed rate of interest until satisfactory completion of the work of demolition.

Assignment or sub-letting

One of the most common reasons for the low esteem in which the Demolition Industry is held by Architects has been the widespread use of sub-contractors who are self-employed or organised into small gangs and who undertake the work of demolition for a price which will take into account income derived from the sale of timber, slates, and other materials from the site. The temptation is, therefore, to finish the work and move on, regardless of regulations, complaints, and the risks involved. The Contract should contain a clause which precludes the assignment or sub-letting of any demolition contract or part thereof, without the written consent of the Architect, always excepting that this permission should not be unreasonably withheld.

Statutory notices

There are a number of statutory and legal notices which may have to be issued or conformed to when undertaking demolition. Often these are assumed to have been fulfilled in respect to notification when the Planning Application for the new building on site is submitted. (Naturally, permission to build must assume that site clearance is required.) Recently, however, several Planning Authorities have announced that this can no longer be just assumed, and that a separate Planning Application must be submitted for demolition only.

At present any building may be demolished, unless it is listed as of special architectural or historic merit under the Town and Country Planning Act, 1971, or is within a Conservation Area as defined by the Town and Country Amenities Act, 1974.

In all cases (in England and Wales, excluding London) before any work commences on site the owner should give notice to the Local Authority as required under Section 29 of the Public Health Act 1961, and the Local Authority may require certain specific actions to be taken. These will usually include:—

a) shoring up any adjacent buildings,

b) weatherproofing any surfaces of adjacent buildings exposed by the work,

c) removing all rubbish and debris resulting from clearance of the site,

d) disconnecting and sealing off any sewer, drain, or waterpipe in or under the building,

e) removing any such sewer or drain,

f) leaving the surface of the site in such a condition as to satisfy the Local Authority.

Similar regulations exist for Scotland (the Building Operators' (Scotland) Regulations 1959), and in the Inner London Area the London Building Act (Amendment) applies.

The Architect should also note that should it be necessary to cross any pavement or public footpath, the Borough Engineer of the respective Local Authority should be approached regarding crossovers. Where skips are to be left on the highway and hoardings or scaffolding erected encroaching on the pavement or highway, various Highway Acts may apply and it will avoid possible delays if these are dealt with before the work is commenced.

If the work is expected to last for more than six weeks, then H.M. Factories Inspectorate should be notified (Factories Act 1961 — Section 127/7).

If demolition work could in any way affect other properties, the Architect should by this stage have reached agreement with adjoining owners on matters of support and protection, etc.

1.3 A Short Explanation of Methods of Demolition

It is not normally considered necessary for the Architect or Engineer to specify the method of demolition to be used, except in very special circumstances. It is useful here, however, to summarise the most widely adopted methods. The British Standard Code of Practice CP 94:1971 Demolition, advises which method should be used for various categories of buildings, and it will be found that the method selected depends on the part of the country in which the project is situated and on what plant the Contractor has available.

First of all, salvageable items are removed, beginning with most fittings, copper, lead and steel piping, domestic fittings, windows and door frames, etc. This commonly-called "stripping out" process continues with the removal of roof coverings and structural timbers generally, in conformity with the old rule that "demolition proceeds in the reverse order of construction".

When the structure has been reduced to basically a brick, masonry, or concrete shell various methods can be used to reduce the building to hardcore or debris which can be loaded up for carting away.

Demolition by hand

This method is usually used for the highest and most inaccessible sections of the work prior to breaking down by machinery, or for complete buildings where access may be not possible for machinery. Operatives use tools of the portable variety, mattocks (in the south of England) or crow-bars (in the north), pneumatic drills, power-saws, etc.

Pulling down by wire rope

In spite of having a number of disadvantages, this method of demolition is probably the one most widely used for masonry and brick structures, which form the bulk of present-day demolition projects. If it is at all possible, all timbers, pipes, beams and lintels should be removed prior to the pulling down operation as a) they may be salvageable, b) they act as stabilisers to the whole building and therefore offer a considerable amount of resistance to demolition, and c) on their removal the building can fall in a much more compact heap. In no case should this method be used where long members are present in the building.

A wire band is set around a portion of the brickwork and is then dragged by a tracked vehicle. As a result it cuts into the brickwork, causing it to collapse. Normally, the same tracked vehicle returns to load the hardcore to be carted off site.

Demolition ball

This method is used in the main for fairly large brick structures and for reinforced concrete buildings, as well as for breaking up mass concrete and reinforced slabs and floors. The ball, which usually weighs half a ton, is dropped vertically onto the structure to be broken, or a sideways motion is imparted to it by swinging or slewing the jib of the crane so that the ball hits the side of the structure. This method requires a higher standard of site supervision than do the methods mentioned above, as the crane operator has to work at some distance from the structure being demolished, and his view of this is restricted. Considerable stresses are imparted to the crane jib, and supervision and maintenance standards must be high. The structure being demolished should be detached from any other building, if necessary by partial hand demolition, before this method is used.

Pusher arm machinery

This method, which has gained in popularity in recent years, involves the use of an extended arm and steel pad fitted to a tracked vehicle in place of the excavator bucket. It is considered that this type of machine is more controllable and in some ways more versatile than the other machinery mentioned above. The pusher arm is placed on the topmost section of a brick wall and forward motion is applied, either by the hydraulic thrust mechanism or by driving the excavator forward.

Deliberate collapse

This method is used in some cases where removal of certain key structural members will cause collapse of the whole or part of the building being demolished. It can be a hazardous operation and very special attention must be paid to ensure that everyone on site is conversant with the procedures being used and is removed to a safe distance when the collapse is imminent.

Explosives

The use of explosives is considered by many experts to be the most economic and quickest method of demolition. It is comparatively rare in Great Britain as many Local Authorities and large concerns exclude the use of explosives on their sites. Generally, the basic principle is that holes

Figure 1   Temporary weatherproofing by means of polythene sheets fixed with battens.

are bored into various supporting sections of the structure and the explosive inserted. When the charges are exploded the structure collapses, breaking up on impact with the ground.

Other methods   There are various machines and types of drills and mechanical breakers which have not been mentioned here. Also more than one or two techniques may sometimes be used on the same site. When the basic structure has been reduced to rubble, the debris should be systematically removed from site or stockpiled for later use if required. The foundations of the buildings are broken up, using manual pneumatic breakers or tractor-mounted weight-dropping breakers.

The site should be fenced off and left clear and tidy to the satisfaction of the Architect.

If temporary weather protection is needed for adjoining exposed walls, prior to final finishing, this is best accomplished by covering them with sarking felt or the more recently available 500 g polythene sheeting. The covering is fixed by battens nailed to the wall.

1.4 Support Works and Treatments to Party Walls Exposed by Demolition

Part 2 of this book provides more details about site supervision, the demolition process, hoardings and fencing. Part 1 continues with some comments on the methods which can be used to provide support for walls which will be exposed by the demolition work, and describes the treatments which such walls will require.

These treatments should already have been agreed upon with adjoining owners (see Chapter 1.1). Essentially they should fulfil two objectives:—

a) provide adequate support for the wall or structure,

b) render the wall weatherproof.

METHODS OF PROVIDING SUPPORT

Temporary support

The erection of shoring is usually carried out as a temporary measure to support the exposed flank wall either until the new building is erected or until satisfactory brick buttressing has been constructed. Shores are normally designed by the Structural Engineer and are often erected by the Demolition Contractor. If, as is sometimes the case, it is necessary to erect them prior to the completion of demolition, the floors and roof of the property to be demolished are removed, the shores are erected and the demolition is carried out with them in position. Such cases are very rare, but when they do occur it is essential that the shores should not be disturbed in any way, and that demolition should be carried out completely by hand.

There are two main types of shoring used, both of which can be constructed of timber. In more recent years, however, more use has been made of standard steel scaffolding.

Raking shores

A raking shore is used to support the wall of buildings adjoining the demolished property when considerable movement or loss of support has occurred as a result of demolition. The components of a typical large timber shore are shown in Figure 2.

A typical sequence of operations for the erection of shores is as follows:—

The exposed wall is examined to ascertain where support is required. Movement is most likely to have taken place as a turning outward at the top due to thrust from the roof timbers, or as a bulge in the centre due to thrust from the weight of the floor loadings of the building still standing.

Figure 2   A typical raking timber shore.

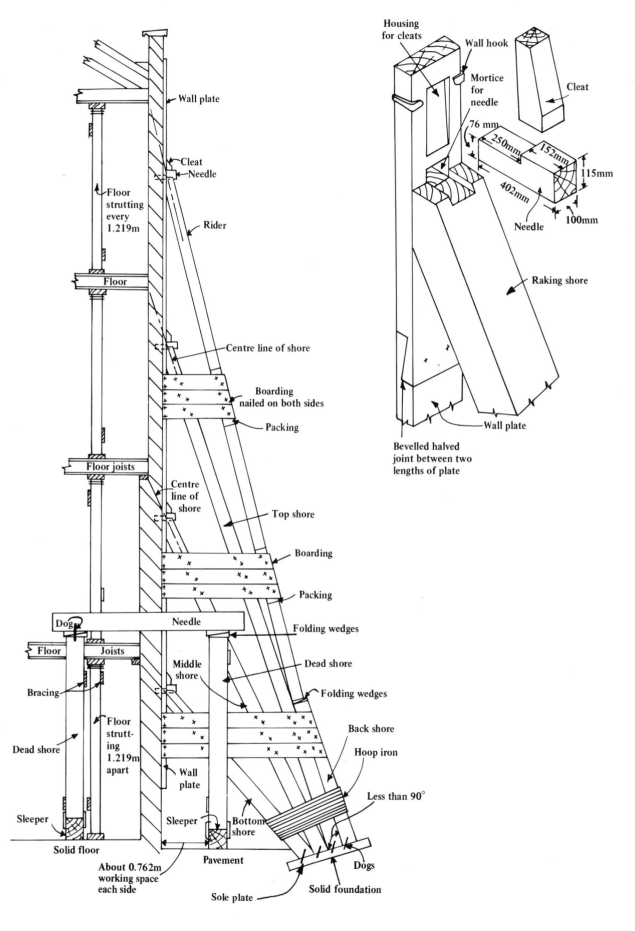

Wall plate

Housing for cleats

Wall hook

Mortice for needle

Cleat

Cleat
Needle

Floor strutting every 1.219m

Rider

76 mm

250mm

152mm

115mm

402mm

100mm

Needle

Raking shore

Floor

Centre line of shore

Boarding nailed on both sides

Packing

Centre line of shore

Top shore

Boarding

Wall plate

Bevelled halved joint between two lengths of plate

Floor joists

Packing

Dog

Needle

Folding wedges

Floor   Joists

Dead shore

Bracing

Middle shore

Folding wedges

Dead shore

Floor strutting 1.219m apart

Wall plate

Back shore

Hoop iron

Sleeper

Sleeper

Bottom shore

Less than 90°

Solid floor

Pavement

About 0.762m working space each side

Sole plate

Solid foundation

Dogs

When it has been decided how many shores are to be erected, an area is excavated at a position determined in accordance with the recommended inclination for this type of shore (maximum 75° : min 45°) and when a solid base has been reached hardcore or concrete is placed to form a foundation. The angled sole plate is then fixed in position.

The wall plate which is to be fixed to the wall is then prepared (a timber wall plate is used for both timber and scaffold shoring and it should be shaped to fit over any bulges or irregularities in the face of the building) and positioned up to the wall. If possible the centre of the plate should coincide with the point of maximum deflection of the wall. A square hole is cut for each of the needles of the shore; these should pass through the plate and project at least 230 mm (9″) into the face of the brickwork.

The rakers of the shoring are then placed in position and spiked together, and the wedges tightened up until the whole shore is stable.

Figure 3   Raking shores in position while a flank wall is being treated.

Flying shores

Flying shores are used when there is a stable building within reach which can be used for support. The great advantage of flying shores is that the site of the demolished building is kept clear. The maximum permissible length of these shores is usually considered to be about 9.0 metres (30 feet), as for lengths greater than this sideways deflection can become a problem. The basic construction of these shores is the same as that of raking shores, and the same type of wall plate is used.

Both raking shores and flying shores made of timber can be tightened by using timber folding wedges which can be hammered in. Discretion should always be used when tightening, as it is not unknown for an unstable wall to be pushed inwards by too enthusiastic tightening.

Permanent support

Brick buttresses

If buttressing to a flank wall is considered necessary, the most convenient way of providing this is to convert the ragged front and rear angle walls of the old structure into buttress form by bonding in brickwork to form piers. The existing foundations should be checked and, if they are satisfactory, the brickwork can be built on these. In older property it may be necessary to excavate and lay suitable pad footings. A damp proof course should be laid to match the one in the existing building, and the top of the buttress should be protected by a weathered coping provided with a drip on the underside. This not only prevents rain penetration but gives protection from staining by rain and snow. It is a good idea to consider whether the piers should be left unrendered, but pointed to provide a feature.

Chimney breasts

Chimney breasts on a flank wall can be conveniently adapted in the following way to assist in providing support to the wall:—

a) the chimney pots should be removed and the openings sealed by a stone or slate slab;

b) the fireplaces should be removed and the flues swept. The openings can then be bricked up, care being taken to bond into the sides of the opening. Air bricks measuring, say, 230 mm (9″) x 230 mm (9″) should be inserted at the top and bottom of the flues to provide ventilation;

c) any timber trimmer joist ends should be removed if possible. If this cannot be done, however, expanded metal lathing can be nailed to cover them;

d) the chimney breasts can now be rendered over or treated with the flank wall.

General points

If there is no parapet wall between properties, it may be necessary to extend the slating or tiling over the flank wall. If this is so, then a 1½ tile or slate course should be provided and a fillet used to tilt the edge tiles up. A drip of at least 50 mm (2″) should be provided where the slate or tiles extend over the flank wall.

In the case of some older cottage properties and very cheaply built terraced houses, it may be found that the walls between houses only extend as far as eaves level. This will mean that they will have to be built up to the underside of the roof coverings. Protection from the weather should be provided to prevent rain entering the roof space, and the brickwork should be completed as quickly as possible to preclude any possibility of a high wind lifting the roof timbers and coverings.

If the condition of the wall is very poor — and on occasions it will be found that some party walls are of virtually rubble construction — it may be more economic to rebuild completely, or to build a facing brick wall outside, and tie it into the old. The new wall should extend over the top of the old one, and special attention should be paid to flashings to ensure that no water can penetrate between the two walls.

WEATHERPROOFING THE WALL

Rendering in cement and sand

Once the structural stability of the newly exposed wall has been ensured — always assuming that the new building is not going to be built up to the wall face — it will be necessary to provide a permanent covering to prevent water penetration.

If the brickwork is of good faced bricks, it may be preferable to rake out the mortar joints, and then repoint in the normal way, but usually the brickwork will be found to be of non-facing bricks, poorly bonded and often with a number of openings which may have to be made good.

Preparation

The wall should be cleaned off completely. All old timber, pipework, nails, plaster and tiling should be hacked off, and the joints of the brickwork raked out to provide a key for rendering. Any small areas of missing brickwork should be filled with salvaged bricks bonded in, and hollows or depressions should be dubbed out.

For a plain rendering, the mix of cement and sand should be porous and weak so that cracking during drying out will be spread over the whole surface. Such a porous rendering will absorb some rainwater but this will not readily be passed to the brickwork and will quickly dry out when wetting stops. It will be an advantage to apply the render in two coats, only the first of these containing a waterproofing agent.

Table 1   Mix proportions by volume.

Mix	Cement	Lime	Sand
A	1	½	4 to 4½
B	1	1	5 to 6
C	1	2	8 to 9

Table 2   Mixes for given backgrounds, exposures and finishes.

Type of finish	First and subsequent undercoats			Finish coat		
	Exposure grading			Exposure grading		
	Severe	Moderate	Sheltered	Severe	Moderate	Sheltered
Wood float	A or B	B or C	B or C	B	B or C	B or C
Scraped or textured	B	B or C	B or C	B	B or C	B or C
Roughcast	A or B	A or B	A or B	— as undercoats —		
Pebble or spar dashed	A	A	A	A	A	A

Figures refer to Table 1 mix nos.

Choice of mix

Each of the two coats should normally be 16 mm (¾″) thick so as to provide 32 mm (1½″) thickness in all. The mixes to be used can be worked out from tables 1 and 2.

These recommendations apply to normal party wall brickwork. In cases of different party wall materials, the relevant Department of the Environment Advisory Leaflet should be consulted.

Finishing coats

The various types of finishing coat are not used as often as they should be. Too often Architects specify plain rendering, though there is a choice of attractive finishes.

Pebble dash or spar dash finish: This is the well-known finish of small pebbles graded from about 6 mm to 13 mm which is thrown on a fresh coat of mortar and left exposed. This finish is particularly suited for use on walls exposed for long periods to driving wind and rain. It needs a strong but plastic mortar to hold the pebbles firmly, and therefore should be used only on a wall where the brickwork is strong and well bonded. In place of pebbles, crushed white stone can be used to produce an attractive finish.

Figure 4 After part of this building had been demolished the flank wall was provided with windows and protected with a spar dash finish.

Rough cast finish: A finish which is thrown on as a wet mix and left rough, so as to give good protection from driving rain. The aggregate in the finish coat is composed of sand and gravel graded from about 6 mm to 13 mm.

Textured finishes: These are produced by treating the freshly applied finishing coat with various different tools, to produce different textures. Examples are torn stucco, stippled stucco and fan texture finish and their local variations, all of which make a finished flank wall far less austere in appearance.

POINTS TO WATCH ON FINISHING A FLANK WALL

The detailing carried out when finishing a flank wall may have a considerable influence on the behaviour and durability of the rendering coat.

Parapets

As parapets are rather severely exposed, they should be provided with copings, drips, and effective damp proof courses beneath the coping, and all features should also be provided with effective drips designed to throw any water clear of the wall.

Top of render coat

If possible, a fillet or metal flashing should be provided at the top of the rendering coat, to prevent water getting behind the coating.

Damp proof course

A common fault when rendering exposed party walls is that the finish

Figure 5   The rendering should not cover the damp proof course, but should be provided with an aluminium or plastic edging stop.

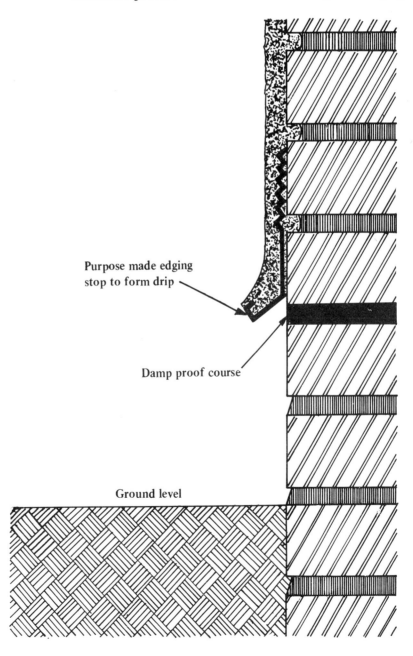

Purpose made edging stop to form drip

Damp proof course

Ground level

at the base of the wall is allowed to bridge a damp proof course.

The damp proof course should always be exposed and marked before rendering is commenced. If the new ground level is to be higher than the damp proof course then a trench should be excavated and a vertical damp proof course inserted. A plastic or metal edging as shown in Fig. 5 should be fixed and a drip formed at the base of the rendering.

An attractive final touch can be applied if the brickwork below the damp proof course can be cleaned and painted with a black bituminous coating.

Part 2

Demolition — on Site

2.1 Techniques and Methods used in the Demolition of Various Types of Structures

Set out in this chapter are guide lines as to the methods and techniques used for the demolition of various groups of structures. Many buildings are made up of several different types of structure, and site conditions vary so much that it is not feasible to really specify one method or another; however, the problems discussed here are those which the Demolition Supervisor is most likely to encounter. General guide lines relating to the safety of men on site and members of the public are given in Chapter 2.3 which should be read in conjunction with the present chapter.

BRICK AND MASONRY BUILDINGS

Houses, factories and other structures built of brick or masonry

It has been found that for the most part buildings made of brick or stone fall into one of two distinct categories, in so far as regards the effect which the construction technique adopted for them has upon any demolition work.

Prior to the 1st World War brickwork was usually made of kiln-fired bricks laid in a mortar of cement and lime. The basic characteristic of this type of brickwork on its demolition is that the lime mortar breaks away easily from the bricks, which often remain in one piece and thus are easily salvaged. The brickwork breaks up very easily and pulling down is fairly simple. However, there is considerable dust raised as the brickwork falls.

The 1920's and onwards saw a considerable increase in the number of buildings constructed in fletton bricks or various faced versions of them, this brickwork being laid in a mortar made of cement, lime, and sand. It is considerably stronger than the lime mortar variety and it may be found that considerable impact or pressure is required to fracture it. When broken both the bricks and mortar fracture together to form large lumps of brickwork. It is in fact virtually impossible to separate bricks from mortar and the lump of brickwork may have to be broken up by hand or small mechanical tools if it is to be of any use even as hardcore. It is therefore considerably more expensive and difficult to deal with the cement-mortar type brickwork than with the older lime-mortar type which usually allows good bricks to be salvaged easily.

The general method of procedure with brick buildings conforms to the general rule that demolition proceeds in the reverse order of construction.

As already stated in chapter 1.3, roof coverings and internal non-structural fittings and timbers should be removed. If the building has a pitched roof, the timbers or trusses should be removed and lowered down to ground level. The building should be demolished by hand to wall plate level. Care should be taken that the stability of any roof trusses is not impaired by the incorrect removal of members in tension. No-one should ever stand on unsupported areas of brickwork, or on brickwork attached to or being supported by that which is being demolished.

The type of house, cottage and factory buildings referred to in this chapter is that which is most common in Britain and, of course, that which forms the object of the vast bulk of demolition contracts at the present time. And yet, though there has been considerable experience in this kind of demolition, it is during the early 'stripping out' process that most accidents occur and most complaints are raised by surrounding residents.

When only the basic brick shell remains, reduced to a safe height by hand demolition or ball and chain, the hardcore can usually be pushed down and loaded directly by most types of bucket-attached excavators.

It is often not even necessary to break up brick footings or concrete strip foundations, for in many cases old buildings have virtually no footings or any they do have are broken up by site machinery.

When the work of demolition and carting away has been completed, the site should always be 'back bladed' by the excavator and as many as possible of the old bricks and pieces of concrete should be removed, so as to leave a tidy cleared site.

Masonry and brick arches

In the case of brick and masonry arches, the basic structural stresses are as shown in Fig. 6a. It can be seen that the imposed load on any arch is transmitted via the arch to the abutments. There is a considerable risk therefore that if support is removed from the abutment before removing the loads caused by the arch (see Fig. 6b), a serious and unexpected collapse may occur. In the case of a viaduct or multi-span arch, the collapse may well move progressively from arch to arch with spectacular and possibly disastrous results. This fairly simple fact is often not appreciated by demolition workers and several accidents have resulted.

It is essential that extra-close supervision is maintained when arches are being demolished, and there should be no hesitation on the part of the Supervisor to insist that temporary centering and shoring be erected to support the arch if there is any doubt at all as to stability or construction (Fig. 6c).

Single span arches can be demolished by hand by carefully taking narrow strips, say 230 mm (1 ft) wide, from the side parallel to the line of the edge of the bridge until only a narrow portion remains which can easily be collapsed.

If this method cannot be undertaken, the method of demolition usually adopted, with or without centering, is as follows (see Figs. 6d and 6e):

a) the spandrel infilling is removed down to the springing line,

b) the arch rings are lifted out and removed,

c) the abutments are demolished.

Figure 6 Demolition procedure for brick and masonry arches.

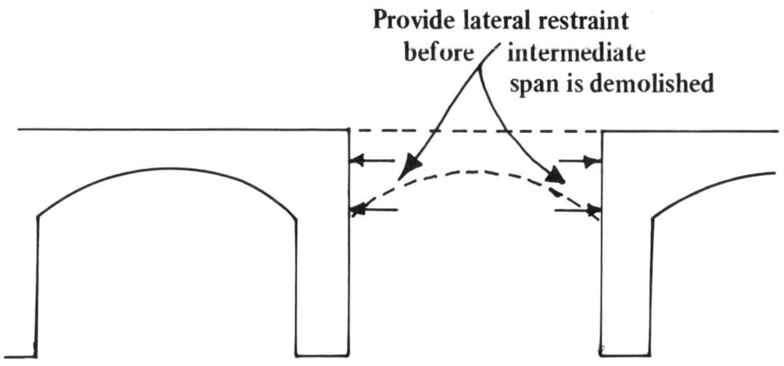

Provide lateral restraint
before / intermediate
span is demolished

(6a)

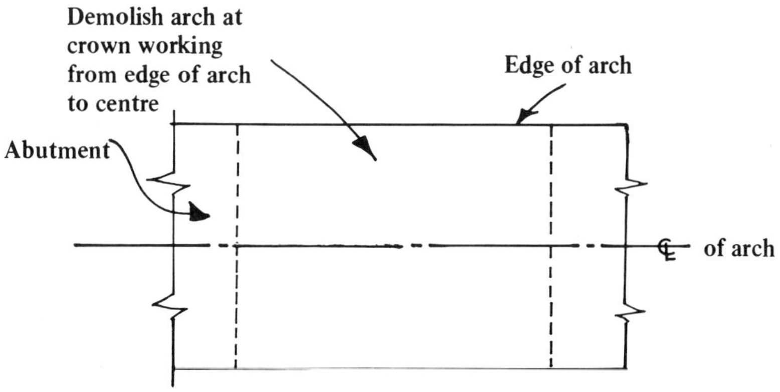

Demolish arch at
crown working
from edge of arch
to centre

Edge of arch

Abutment

(6b)

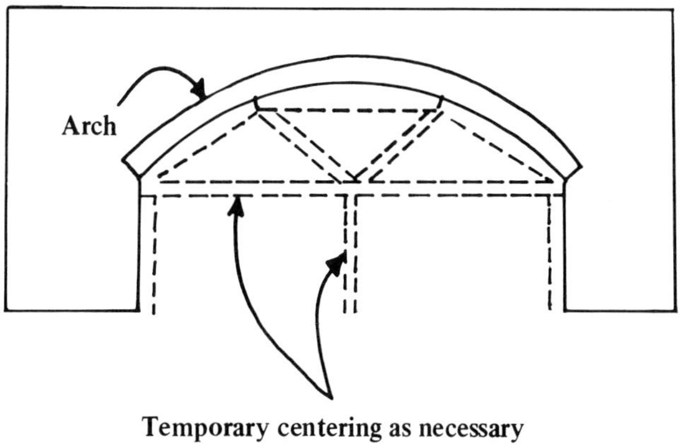

℄ of arch

Arch

(6c)

Temporary centering as necessary

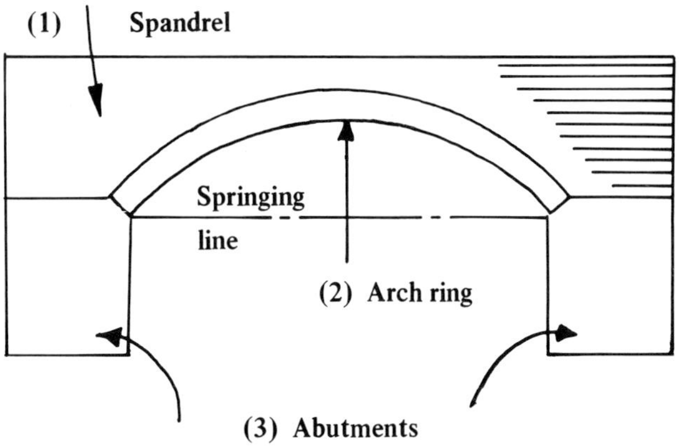

(1) | Spandrel

Springing
line

(2) Arch ring

(6d)

(3) Abutments

Figure 6 Demolition procedure for brick and masonry arches (cont.)

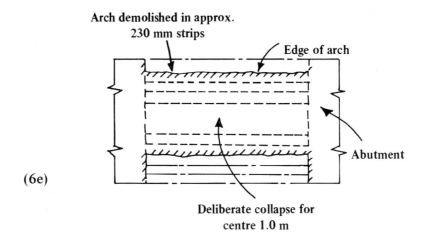

(6e)

Arch demolished in approx. 230 mm strips

Edge of arch

Abutment

Deliberate collapse for centre 1.0 m

Figure 7a An elevated roadway immediately prior to demolition.

Figure 7b   During the course of demolition.

Figure 7c   A demolition ball is being used to break down the series of brick arches. In the background can be seen a scaffold around the base of a chimney shaft. The shaft is being demolished by digging the brickwork off and allowing it to drop down the shaft. This type of scaffold should only be used when, as in this case, the area around the base is fenced and access is limited to demolition operatives.

In the case of many old bridges and arches, the spandrels and tops of the abutments are filled with rubble or mass concrete and considerable force may have to be used to break the fill. If there is any likelihood of vibration, centering should be used.

When the site is fairly isolated and the bridge spans a road or railway line which does not have to remain in use during the period of demolition, the most practical way to demolish it is to break the crown of the arch down by a demolition ball attached to a crane standing off the bridge.

Brick and masonry arches are the type of structure most suited to demolition by explosives. When the use of explosives is planned for a multi-span viaduct or other structure, it is preferable that this be charged to collapse completely when blasted. This is to ensure that further charges do not have to be placed in the vicinity of what may have become a very unsafe semi-demolished structure.

STRUCTURES WITH STEEL FRAMES OR COMPONENTS

Roof trusses

In virtually all designs of both timber and steel roof trusses, the truss is planned to support the loads to be imposed on it only when acting as a complete unit. Such loads are principally the self-weight of the roof coverings and any loadings imposed on them. These loads plus the self-weight of the trusses all combine to tend to force the top of the vertical wall stanchions apart, and it is the job of the horizontal member to resist these combined loads. It is thus held in a state of tension as shown in the diagrammatic sketch in Fig. 8; it is obvious that to sever this main tie is to invite collapse of possibly both the roof and the walls of the structure.

Figure 8 Forces in a pitched roof truss.

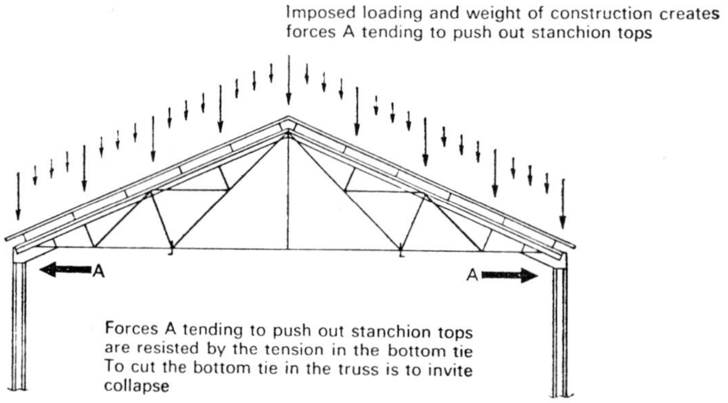

Imposed loading and weight of construction creates forces A tending to push out stanchion tops

A — — A

Forces A tending to push out stanchion tops are resisted by the tension in the bottom tie To cut the bottom tie in the truss is to invite collapse

The dismantling of roof trusses should therefore be carried out strictly in the reverse order of the method of erection, and no indiscriminate cutting should be allowed. Work should therefore proceed as follows:

a) the structure should be braced or shored temporarily;

b) the roof claddings should be removed and carefully lowered to the ground;

c) the truss should be supported by a suitable crane or roped up;

d) if the span is a large one, as for example in Fig. 8, to lift the truss may put compressive stresses on the main tie, and cause it to buckle.

It may, therefore, be necessary to brace the tie with heavy timbers or girders splinted along the component;

e) the purlins on either side of the truss should be removed, and the bolts connecting the truss to the side walls or stanchions disconnected;

f) the truss should be lowered to the ground and dismantled.

Steelwork — general

The first step in dismantling both framed and unframed steel structures is to unbolt the joints or cut them by various means, and then to lower the components to the ground. It is essential that operatives wear safety harnesses at all times as, due to settlement or structural damage, the joints of a framed building often spring apart when released.

Any cladding on the steelwork should be removed as early as possible as very considerable wind loads can be exerted on the structure, and it should be remembered that steel frames are designed to be kept stable by forces being balanced throughout the complete structure.

Isolated steel columns or stanchions should be carefully guyed with ropes or supported by cranes when the holding-down bolts are sheared, then carefully lowered to the ground.

Bridges and gantries of steel construction

The first stage of demolition for all bridges is to remove the dead load of road metalling or railway tracks and ballast. The bridge decking and any fittings or non-structural sections can also be removed. The side girders of the bridge should be supported by temporary fixings to ensure that they remain vertical when the ends are cut away. Care should be taken when selecting suitable points to begin the cutting to ensure that the ends cannot slide off the abutments, and there should be no possibility of the bridge twisting or collapsing.

It has been found from experience that in most cases bridge sections and girders can be lifted out in their entirety and transferred to a suitable point at ground level for cutting up. Where this does not appear to be a practical proposition the bridge members can sometimes be pulled back along the line of the road over their supporting structures.

If the crane lifting method is selected, consideration should be given to the feasibility of using purpose-made brackets which can be bolted to

Figure 9 Purpose-made brackets being used to lift out steel bridge girders.

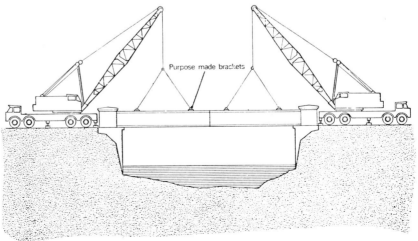

Purpose made brackets

girders to avoid the need for slings. The ends of the girders should be jacked up to break the bearing seal and then the crane should begin to lift the girders down.

When two cranes are required to sling together as shown in Fig. 9, a signalling system must be established and a competent person must act as supervisor to ensure that loads are evenly distributed and that no sideways drag is created which could overturn one of the cranes.

Figure 10   Two cranes lift down the side girders of a disused railway bridge.

Figure 11   Loading bridge girders direct onto lorries.

It should be noted that when the bridge being demolished spans water and the operatives working on it may run the risk of falling in, certain requirements relating to fencing and rescue equipment — set out in the Construction (General Provisions) Regulation 1961 — must be conformed with.

Many steel and iron bridges have been continuously maintained over the years by periods of painting, so cutters working with oxy-acetylene equipment may be in danger of breathing high lead content fumes, and there is even the possibility of small fires being caused. Whilst these problems can be overcome, they can seriously delay progress on some jobs and this should be kept in mind when tendering for work of this kind.

REINFORCED CAST IN-SITU STRUCTURES

Both structures built of precast units of reinforced concrete and those built of reinforced concrete cast in-situ have increased considerably in quantities in recent years, and growing numbers of these are now becoming liable for demolition. It has been found that because of the expensive machinery required to break up the material in question, coupled with the very small amount of salvageable materials produced, this is the most expensive sector of the demolition industry.

Figure 12a   A demolition ball breaks up a reinforced concrete silo.

Figure 12b The concrete breaks away from the reinforcement, falls to the bottom of the silo and is removed. The reinforcement is later cut up to manageable lengths by means of oxyacetylene torches.

If it is at all possible, details of the type and positioning of reinforcement should be obtained from drawings, and special attention should be paid to ascertain whether any sections are vital for structural stability.

The following notes cover various types of component. It should be remembered, however, that many buildings are constructed of various combinations of columns, floor slabs, and beams, etc., and some of a mix of cast in-situ and precast units, so that only general techniques can be covered.

Suspended reinforced concrete slabs

Reinforced concrete slabs and unreinforced hollow pot floors should be demolished by cutting with compressor guns, hydraulic bursters and oxy-acetylene equipment, parallel to the line of the main reinforcement, thus reducing the slab to small sections. If the direction of reinforcement cannot be located on drawings, small trial holes can be cut in the floor at suitable positions. When possible, the cutting work should be carried out from an independent platform spanning the main support beams, as shown in Fig. 13a. The temptation to allow the cutting down of large sections should be resisted; in fact the strips cut away should be no more than 300 mm (12″) wide.

Reinforced concrete beams

All loads these beams are carrying should be removed before any demolition is commenced. Supporting ropes or shores should then be fixed to support each beam, and the reinforcement at the ends exposed by compressor guns. Next the reinforcement should be cut at one end and that end lowered to the ground, leaving the other, fixed end supported by the ropes or shores (see Fig. 13b). Lastly the reinforcement is cut at the second end also and the whole beam is lowered to the ground for breaking up.

Figure 13a   Demolition of reinforced concrete floors.

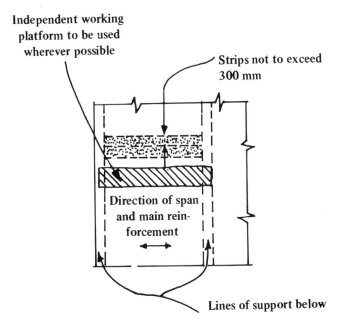

Figure 13b   Demolition of reinforced concrete beams.

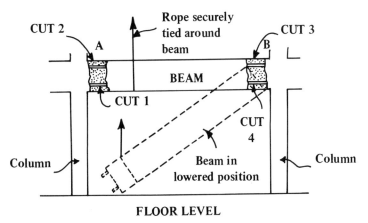

Figure 13c   Demolition of reinforced concrete columns.

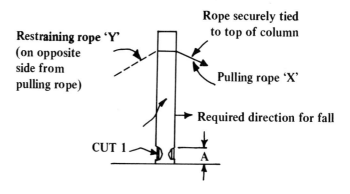

Figure 13d   Demolition of reinforced concrete walls.

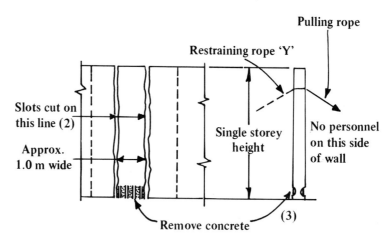

Reinforced concrete columns

All weights and loads supported by the column should be removed so that only the self-weight of this is acting upon it. Two wire ropes should then be fixed to the top of the column to provide support and the reinforcement bars should be exposed by compressor guns, as near to the base as possible. These should be cut on the opposite side of the column from the rope which has been selected for pulling (Fig. 13c). The column is then pulled over by machine or winch, using the second rope as a steadying line, and lowered to the ground for breaking up.

Reinforced concrete walls

Constructions of this type are best dealt with by cutting them into manageable sections and then treating these as a series of columns (see Fig. 13d).

PRE-STRESSED AND POST-TENSIONED CONCRETE BEAMS AND STANCHIONS

This group of structures can be divided into two basic types:—

Structures made of precast units. A structure of this type is composed of a number of concrete units with the tendon under a factory-applied stress. The various components are bolted or fixed with bars and grouted together on site.

Structures made of post-tensioned units. The unit is cast on site and the tendon within the beam is subjected to progressive tension by tightening a sliding bolt at the end of the beam.

Many modern structures are a combination of both these types of units. It is emphasized that, owing to limited practical experience, very little information is available on how to proceed with their demolition, and a Chartered Structural Engineer should always investigate the construction, even before inspection holes are cut.

The post-tensioned method was formulated to enable loads to be carried over a much longer span by a more slender member. In this case the greatest danger arises when the tendon is ungrouted and the tension was applied progressively as the loads above were being applied to the beam. The main hazard lies in the fact that when the load is removed by demolition the beam can fail in an upward direction due to the forces inherent in the highly tensioned tendon. Even if the tendon has been post-tensioned only to a force slightly in excess of the overall downward stress, there are considerable dangers if it is cut, for the anchorage bolts are released with tremendous force. It is by no means certain that it is any safer when the tendon is grouted in, for it should be remembered that the function of the grout is to protect the tendon from corrosion and not to hold it in any way.

If it is at all possible, the members should be lowered to the ground for inspection, without breaking any inspection holes, and then investigation and dismantling should proceed under expert guidance.

The following three methods have been postulated for relieving the tensions within the beams:—

a) Reach the tendons and hold them, then cut through the concrete to form small sections and gradually allow the tendons to take up a shorter path.

b) Apply heat so that the tendons weaken and expand. This allows the concrete to be broken up progressively.

c) In some types of construction, the tendons are held in ducts created by spaces between the top and bottom flanges, and the tendon forms a curved outline, thus providing support at the centre of the beam. In such cases it is possible to break the ducts and gradually allow the tendons to rise and take a shorter path, thus gradually relieving the tensile stress.

All of these methods are comparatively untried, and it is obvious that considerably more research will be needed before a really comprehensive procedure can be formulated.

CHIMNEY SHAFTS OF BRICK OR MASONRY

Any chimney shaft or similar tall, slender structure to be demolished should, of course, be carefully surveyed and inspected before work is started. Particular attention should be paid to ladders, climbing irons, and bonds. It should also be noted that on occasions brickwork at the lower regions of industrial chimney shafts can be extremely weak, due to the action of deleterious acidic fumes produced by furnaces.

Hand demolition

Hand demolition should be carried out from a working platform supported by either an internal or an external platform. If there is any doubt about the condition or security of fixed ladders or climbing irons, then steeplejacks should be employed to ladder the chimney. Demolition should proceed course by course, the debris being dropped either inside the shaft, or outside it if the site is a clear one. It is important that rubble should not be allowed to accumulate inside or outside the shaft and thereby impose pressures on the base of the structure as this may cause collapse.

Demolition by deliberate collapse

Bringing down the chimney by deliberate collapse is a spectacular and very economical method of demolition. It can, however, be undertaken only when conditions are favourable, that is:—

a) there should be a clear space for the fall of at least 1½ times the total height of the chimney;

b) considerable vibration may be set up as the chimney falls, so there should be no sewers or underground services on the line of the fall;

c) lookouts should be on site; and a warning signal should be arranged, to be used when collapse is imminent.

Deliberate collapse is started by systematic hand cutting commencing at a point on the line of the proposed fall and proceeding around both sides simultaneously. Vertical laths are positioned in the cavity to act as a warning system; when these bend and dust begins to fall the chimney is about to collapse and workmen should retire to safety.

An old method used to be for the brickwork to be removed and progressively shored up with timber supports which were then burnt out so that collapse took place. This method is not recommended now, because if insufficient brickwork has been removed or if the timbers fail to burn satisfactorily, the Contractor is then obliged to approach an unstable and dangerous structure.

The use of explosives is a convenient way of setting off deliberate collapse on an isolated site. Sections of the base are first removed by hand demolition, leaving the chimney standing on four brick 'legs'. Charges are placed in holes drilled in these 'legs' and fired. The chimney in effect 'squats' and crumbles from the bottom as the brickwork hits the ground. Though this is a convenient method of demolition, a considerable amount of vibration is produced, and caution should be taken if there is any likelihood of its causing damage.

CHIMNEY SHAFTS IN REINFORCED CONCRETE

In more recent years chimney shafts have been constructed of reinforced concrete, usually with a refractory brick lining. The concrete is a continuous reinforced tube constructed by using a sliding former which is jacked up as the concrete is poured. If the chimney shaft is post-tensioned, a Chartered Engineer should be consulted, but if normal reinforced concrete construction has been used, a working platform should be set up. The concrete should be cut into panels of a manageable size which should then be lowered to the ground for breaking up. Whilst the concrete is being cut by compressor guns and the reinforcement by oxy-acetylene equipment, the section being dealt with should be supported. The refractory brick lining can usually be easily broken up and the debris allowed to fall down the shaft where it should be removed progressively. Like brick chimney shafts these structures are ideally suited to demolition by explosives, provided the site is isolated.

PETROLEUM AND CHEMICAL STORAGE TANKS

Techniques and dangers of removal

There is an increasing number of buildings being demolished which have held fuel oil or petroleum storage tanks. These may be above ground, although the larger tanks are often underground, surrounded either by a bed of sand — in older garages, or by mass concrete — in more recent buildings. The Petroleum Licensing Officer of the Local Authority in which the petroleum storage tanks are situated can normally provide details, as in most cases the tanks will have had to be licensed.

As soon as possible, even before any demolition work commences within the vicinity, the tanks should be emptied of fuel and as far as possible rendered free of any potentially dangerous liquids or gases. The most commonly used method, and the most simple is for the tank to be stripped of its associated pipework (the tools used should be of non ferrous metal and carefully handled to avoid sparks), and then filled with water which should be kept running until it discharges from all holes and ventilation openings in the tank. Some tanks in garages are compartmented and care should be taken to ensure that all the compartments are filled.

There are two other methods which can be used if supplies of water are scarce or if the very heavy weight of this would cause difficulties.

a) An inert gas, normally nitrogen or carbon dioxide (CO_2), can be piped continuously into the tank, the mixture of fumes and gases passing out through a specific opening, until the tank can be considered purged.

b) The other method which is sometimes used is to place small pieces of solid carbon dioxide (dry ice) into the tank. These in effect melt and fill the tank with carbon dioxide gas. It should be noted that H.M. Factory Inspectorate is not very happy with this method as it has been found that the carbon dioxide layers very heavily in the bottom of the tank, and of course if the tank is left sealed, when the time comes for it to be cut into sections, operatives find themselves working in an asphyxiating atmosphere.

When any liquids or gases remaining in it have been rendered inert, the tank should be exposed and lifted out of the ground or from its supports. A warning stating DANGER — PETROL TANK should be painted prominently in red on its sides and ends.

It should be remembered that the sand fill or earth around the tank may well have been contaminated by leakage over the years, so smoking, naked lights, and fires should not be allowed within the area and warning notices to this effect should be erected.

Throughout all the above works, no petroleum or liquid chemicals should be allowed to enter any drains or sewers.

When the tank has been removed to a suitable site, it should be cut up as soon as possible and disposed of as scrap. This is a dangerous operation and the possibility of explosion should never be underestimated, so fires and naked lights should still not be allowed near the tank.

There is always the possibility that volatile residues or liquids remaining in the tank may still be dangerous, and the method of water displacement should again be used. It is considered by experienced demolition supervisors that the best way to start demolishing the tank is to carefully unbolt the inspection plate, which is usually at the top of the tank, as the fumes always collect at this point. If this is not possible, the top section of the tank should be cut open with hand-operated metal saws, care being taken not to produce any sparks.

Most fuel oil tanks are of comparatively thin gauge metal sheet, so a crude method which can occasionally be employed for their demolition is to smash the tank with a demolition ball. This normally splits the seams and enables any fumes to escape.

It appears that foam-making equipment can be used with considerable success in this field. A medium or high expansion foam is pumped into the tank from the bottom and allowed to overflow for a while. The tank is kept full of foam whilst the walls and top are being cut. Research is still being carried out on this method, but indications are that it will provide a way of dealing with tanks while these are still in position, which could be of great importance when demolishing factories and other industrial premises.

PARTIAL DEMOLITION

When only part of a building is to be demolished, special precautions should be taken to ensure that as little damage as possible is caused to the section that is to remain. That is:–

a) the structural stability of the building to remain should be checked by the Architect and any necessary temporary shoring should be organised;

b) all openings into the section to remain should be sealed to prevent dust percolation;

c) any pipework, girders, or timbers attached to the main building should be cut off as close to the line of demolition as possible;

d) all electricity and telephone cables and gas pipes should be checked and sealed off at the point of entry;

e) any temporary weatherproofing required should, if possible, be carried out before demolition commences.

2.2 New Methods and Equipment

As was stated in the previous chapter, the biggest problem facing the Demolition Contractor is the demolition of reinforced concrete structures. Considerable research is being carried out in this field and new techniques are being tested which will, it is hoped, enable reinforced concrete and mass concrete to be broken up or cut more easily.

Hydraulic burster

The hydraulic burster is the most successful innovation to date. Holes are drilled into the concrete to be demolished and the burster — which consists of a steel cylinder — is inserted into each of these in turn. A number of pistons are forced out of the cylinder under hydraulic pressure and these break the concrete along the line of the pre-drilled holes. The big advantages of this equipment are its low noise level and the fact that no sparks are produced. Two operations are required, however; that is, the drilling of the holes and the insertion of the cylinders, thus the method is fairly slow.

Gas expansion burster

This piece of equipment, which is most suited for the demolition of mass concrete, consists of a steel cylinder containing chemicals which vapourise and expand rapidly — thereby applying considerable force — when triggered off by an electrical charge. It is used in a similar way to the hydraulic burster, in that holes are drilled into the concrete and the burster rods are inserted. When these are fired, the released gas expansion breaks the concrete. Although there is no risk of flying debris with this method, as with explosives, precautions must always be taken to protect personnel against any possible structural collapse or falling masonry.

Thermic lances

The thermic lance, which was first used in military engineering prior to the Second World War and which is now produced by a number of specialist firms, consists of a steel tube with an internal steel rod. After the end has been heated, oxygen is passed down the tube, causing the steel to burn at a very high temperature. The more recently invented plasma arc lance makes use of different metals, but with both types of equipment both concrete and reinforcement are burnt and melted away at a fairly high rate. This method is fairly expensive and considerable smoke and fumes are produced which have to be extracted from the working area. Hot slag is also produced and this must be prevented from dripping onto lower floors. The lance burns away at a fairly rapid rate and the intense heat engendered means that surrounding members can sometimes suffer expansion damage.

Other developments

Big improvements have also been made in recent years with attachments for existing machinery, one of the most useful being the hydraulically operated concrete hammer which can be fixed to the end of the jib of an excavator.

The biggest need is still for a machine which can break masonry and concrete structures more quietly; also a cheaper method for breaking mass concrete roads is still urgently required.

The Building Research Station is developing a device to mount on site vehicles which, it is expected, will be capable of breaking concrete noiselessly by applying bending stress. At the date of preparation of this volume details have not been released, but it is understood that the results obtained from the initial tests of an experimental machine are promising.

2.3 Safety Guide Lines

PROTECTION OF MEN ON SITE

The number of accidents in the Building Industry, and the Demolition Sector in particular, to men on site is extremely high, and most authorities are of the opinion that this number could be considerably reduced by better supervision and organisation. Such accidents can be listed in the following order of incidence:—

a) falls of persons on site,

b) accidents caused by:

    i) falling materials or sections of structures,
    ii) unintentional collapse of parts of buildings,
    iii) lifting operations and unprotected machinery,
    iv) fires and explosions (this refers to unintentional explosions of gases, etc.),
    v) electric shocks,
    vi) lifts, obstructed accesses, etc.

It is obvious that many men engaged in demolition work will not be conversant with the structural nature of what is being taken down, and guidance in this respect should be competent and continuous. The supervision of demolition should only be entrusted to someone who is widely experienced not only in demolition but also in building construction.

The Supervisor should, if possible, examine any plans there are of the properties being demolished; if, as so often happens, none are available, he should make his own survey.

The first task to be carried out on site is to ensure that services have been disconnected and made safe over the whole site to be cleared. The disconnections are almost always carried out by the appropriate supply authority or sometimes under their direction, but it is always good practice to check both visually and also, if possible, with the Authority direct.

A plan of the proposed sequence of operations should be formulated and explained to and discussed with site operatives.

Various points and problems may arise as demolition proceeds, and these are briefly as follows.

The 'stripping out' process

1.   Whenever possible, windows should be taken out to avoid damage being caused by broken glass. Window frames should be left in to help to maintain the strength of walls.

2. Windows and door openings should be boarded up.

3. Internal entrances to lift shafts should be barricaded.

4. The approaches to all areas where flooring has been removed should be barricaded to indicate the need for special care and the possibility of danger.

5. Balconies and cantilever masonry projections should be cut down and the debris removed before the main demolition commences.

6. Any metal staircases or ladders should be inspected before use and access to them should be closely controlled.

7. Neither stone nor concrete staircases should be used, once they have been disturbed, as in many cases the bearing areas are very small, and even a small movement can lead to collapse.

8. Staircases should be kept free from debris.

9. Any timber removed from the buildings being demolished should be carefully stacked, and projecting nails and screws should be removed, whenever possible.

10. The condition of any adjacent properties which may be affected by the demolition, and the relationship of these to the buildings being demolished should be pointed out to operatives.

The preliminary 'stripping out' process should continue until roof coverings, fittings, pipework, and generally all non-structural parts of the building have been removed. Roof trusses and timbers should be lifted down, and as far as possible only steel, concrete or brickwork should remain.

The demolition of the remainder of the building should now proceed in accordance with the general principles set out in Chapter 2.1, until the structure has been reduced to rubble or easily removable sections.

Whichever one of the following methods is used, the Supervisor should ensure that the basic principles are conformed to and that all the points mentioned are checked. It should be noted that these are general points which may relate to more than one section, not only that in which they have been placed.

Demolition by hand

The structures being demolished should already have had the floors removed or at least openings cut in them. Rubble and debris should never be allowed to build up and overload the floors (in many cases already weakened by woodworm or rot) as this may cause collapse, nor should debris be piled against walls where lateral pressure may cause failure. Instead, all rubble and debris should be lowered to the ground or sent down 'dog-leg' chutes and constantly cleared so as to avoid build up.

Operatives should not be allowed to stand on the brickwork which they are demolishing, or on any member supported by that brickwork.

On completion of each day's work, the buildings being worked on should be left in a stable condition, without any overhanging brickwork or timbers.

Pulling down by wire rope

The Supervisor should ensure that the wire ropes used in this operation are checked regularly and that they have secure fixings at either end.

When using this method, or any other involving the use of mobile machinery, the Supervisor should ensure that operatives remain in safe positions.

If, for any reason, the machine or band is found to be inadequate to achieve complete collapse, then a pusher arm or ball should be used to finish the work, as the structural stability of the structure may well have been undermined.

Demolition ball

The operator should be fully trained and experienced in the use of the equipment, and care should be taken to ensure that the manufacturers' recommendations for the weight of the ball, and the slew and radius of the crane jib should not be exceeded. All safety devices should be in full working order.

The ball should always be used with a drag line so that it can be kept under control. Slewing with the ball should not exceed the 30^n permitted by B.S. Code of Practice CP 94:1971.

The cab of the crane should be robust enough to withstand impact and any glass must be laminated.

The machine must always stand on firm, even ground. All operatives should leave the demolition area before the ball is put into use, and they should stay well clear while it is being used. No person should be allowed to approach a partially demolished structure until the ball has made a tidy break in the work, thus removing any danger of local collapse.

Pusher arm machinery

When used by a skilled operator, this type of machine is considered to be more controllable than any other demolition device, since the debris normally falls away from the operator.

The pusher arm pad should be placed against the wall at no more than 600 mm (2 ft) from the top of the wall. The use of the machine is therefore restricted by the height of the building. The machine should always stand on level ground and the temptation to allow it to work from raised banks of debris in order to gain height should be resisted. The cabin should be robust and fitted with a guard to protect the driver from impact with debris.

Deliberate collapse

This is sometimes a very economical method of demolition but there are several dangers to watch for:—

The building may collapse to a greater extent than was intended.

An engineered collapse may fail to take place, leaving the structure in a dangerous condition.

Small parts of the structure may be thrown for considerable distances and so cause injuries. As a general rule, no person should approach nearer than a distance equal to twice the height of the structure.

This method is sometimes selected for taking down wooden structures, in which case the Supervisor should look for any rot or decay in the timbers which might cause premature failure. It should, of course, be kept in mind that there is no advantage in deliberate collapse if the debris is going to be so chaotic that demolition by other methods would result in a site which would be easier to clear up.

Explosives

Demolition by explosives should only be entrusted to specialist firms with known experience in this field. The use of explosives in the Services

61

General precaut essarily be regarded as a qualification for

ind the following general principles and

plosives Acts of 1875 and 1923 and
g to storage and conveyance of

en who are at least 21 years of age

of dangerous shrapnel through
ur mild steel.

In general, when explosives are being used on the site, the Supervisor should check that the following precautions are taken:—

1) safe escape routes should be pre-arranged;
2) members of the public and animals must be kept at a safe distance;
3) a warning system should be pre-arranged and understood by all men working on the site;
4) even more importance than usual should be attributed to advance planning, good supervision and good teamwork;
5) protection should be provided against flying debris and the effects of shock waves;
6) a set routine should be organised for the examination of misfires;
7) electric detonators should be used, but kept well distant until the last moment when the charge is connected.

If the Supervisor ensures that all the preceding rules are complied with, he should have a tidy, safe, and economic site. When using the newer techniques he should also pay attention to the considerations mentioned in Chapter 2.2, and of course he can learn much from the observation of other sites.

Finally, there are some general points to be observed which can make all the difference between having a well run site or a poorly run one.

1. All site operatives should be provided with protective clothing and equipment. Everyone should be encouraged to wear safety boots, helmets, goggles, and safety harnesses whenever necessary. It is understood that the new Safety Regulations proposed by the Government will make the wearing of goggles mandatory, but this has not been confirmed at the time of writing.

2. Supervisors should keep a constant watch for the presence of dangerous materials on site, and also keep up to date with literature on new products and techniques and their dangers.

The most dangerous of all asbestos products to be found in buildings is crocidolite (blue asbestos), and in most cases this can be recognised by its colour (it may be found as a spray on the underside of roofs). If, however, any form of loose asbestos is found, under the Asbestos Regulations 1969 it should be reported to H.M. District Inspector of Factories whose advice should be taken. Some rubber foams and fabrics can also be dangerous when burnt and the Supervisor should be conversant with the problems they raise.

3. Oxygen, acetylene, and other gas bottles should be securely locked away each night or taken off site to a central store. After use they should be returned to the store as soon as possible, as even when empty they are dangerous if exposed to heat.

PROTECTION OF THIRD PARTIES

Hoardings

If the site is in a built-up area or any other place where there may be a possibility of members of the public being injured, the Architect should insist on its being protected by adequate hoardings throughout the period of demolition. These are often made of a salvaged timber framework covered by either salvaged floor boarding or corrugated iron sheeting. A

Figure 14 Pre-made hoardings constructed of sections of shuttering grade plywood, front and rear views.

typical specification and drawings of sample hoardings are shown in
Appendix 3.

If a considerable proportion of a Contractor's work is carried out within
city areas, these temporary hoardings can be constructed of sheets of
shuttering grade plywood which can then be recovered on completion of
each job. Figs. 14a and 14b show a typical hoarding of this sort in a busy
city street. It will be noted that heavy salvaged sleepers have been used to
protect and form a footway for pedestrians at the base of the hoarding.

Lighting should be provided on corners and ends of the hoarding if
necessary, but if electricity is used, it should be limited to 25 volts in
order to avoid accidents.

Notices warning the public that work is in progress should be erected
at various places. It should be remembered that members of the public
are invariably attracted by demolition and sometimes attempt to get far
closer than is safe. Even on entirely isolated sites, barriers and warning
notices should be erected.

Illegal tipping of rubbish on site

The illegal tipping and dumping of rubbish on site has become an increasing problem in recent years, especially in the South of England, where
the cost and difficulties of finding suitable tipping land are growing prohi-
bitive. There are many, often self-employed, one-truck, lorry owners who
contract to remove soil or rubbish from building sites at a cheap rate. The
load is tipped quickly on any nearby, vacant site and the unmarked lorry
disappears smartly. It is usually very difficult to catch these 'fly-tippers' and
the penalties for the offence committed are in no way severe enough to
prevent 'fly-tipping' being a very profitable operation. The best protection
against them is for a good quality fence to be erected around the site and
maintained there throughout the contract.

Protective fans

When any two or more storeyed building is to be demolished, fans
should be erected around it to protect passers-by from falling masonry.

**Figure 15   A simple fan constructed of timbers salvaged from the build-
ings being demolished.**

Figure 16 A fan constructed of scaffolding. Note the dust-sheets which have been hung underneath.

One fan at first floor level should be sufficient for a three storey building, while buildings higher than this usually require additional fans at alternate floor levels. Most fans are made of scaffolding, but sometimes salvaged timber is used. Typical examples are shown in Figs. 15 and 16. As a general rule, they should have a minimum width of 10 scaffold boards and a splayed upstand a minimum of 4 boards high. It should be remembered that their object is to prevent debris from falling, not to store hardcore, and any debris caught by them should be cleared away immediately to prevent overloading. Whenever possible, staircases should be left in to provide access to them (note, however, comments made about staircases earlier in this chapter with reference to the stripping out process); if ladders are required, they should be tied, if possible.

Scaffolding

In the case of stone clad or decorated buildings situated in certain restricted locations, it may be necessary to erect scaffolding to enable the work to proceed without any debris being made, or any disturbance being caused to pedestrians and vehicular traffic.

The scaffold should be of heavy-duty, independent type, with additional ties into the building, and it should be gradually reduced in height as demolition proceeds. The erection of the scaffolding should be carried out in accordance with British Standard Code of Practice CP 97, 1967 Metal Scaffolding. If the Architect has any doubt about the ability of the Demolition Contractor to erect scaffolding, it can be a good idea for him to insist that this work be done by a specialist sub-contractor approved by himself.

Once erection has been completed and demolition is under way, the Supervisor should keep a close eye on the scaffold and arrange for it to be altered as necessary as the work proceeds. A scaffold should be inspected every seven days and at other times in certain circumstances specified in the Construction Regulations 1966.

Some of the most important points to be checked in inspecting a scaffold are:—

a) that the standards are correctly aligned,

b) that there has been no undermining of base plates and that they are adequately supported,

c) that no sections of the building which supported parts of the scaffold have been removed,

d) that couplers are secured and tightened and boards are sound,

e) that guard rails and toe boards are in place,

f) that ladders are in good condition and properly supported.

Dust sheets

If the pulling down process is likely to produce dust, tarpaulin sheets should be hung from the top of the scaffold down to the hoarding, and, if necessary, water can be sprayed from hoses inside the scaffold.

Fires on site

Considerable damage is caused and a vast number of complaints are generated by indiscriminate or careless lighting of fires on site. Indeed, in recent years some insurance companies have refused to cover damage caused by bonfires on site. Many local authorities and large firms are concerned about this and their contract documents usually contain clauses which restrict or completely ban burning on site. The Clean Air Acts do have exemptions, which mean that building sites are not subject to the Act provided that the fires are lit under controlled conditions. The fire should be watched over by a workman at all times, and a hose pipe should always be available for emergencies. The Supervisor should keep a tight control over the lighting of fires. Under no circumstances should timbers be burnt in the building being demolished, but they should always be removed to a suitable position.

Leaving the site

Before leaving the site at the end of the day, the Supervisor should make the habit of checking up on all aspects of the work, paying particular attention to the following:—

a) *The security of buildings and site machinery:* All demolition sites are an attraction to children and vandals, so as far as possible buildings should be secured against entry and left in a safe condition. Considerable damage has been caused by the malicious starting up of excavators and similar equipment by children, so all machinery should be immobilised or removed to a safe and secure area.

b) *Fires on site:* All fires should be extinguished well before the end of the day's work.

c) *Fencing:* All fencing should be intact.

Appendix 1

Pre-demolition Check List for Architects and Supervisors

Given below is a list of items to check when a demolition contract is being undertaken.

ITEMS TO BE CHECKED BY THE ARCHITECT

A)   Before the work commences:

Ownership and legal matters

a) *Freehold and leasehold interests*
   — Have they all been transferred to the Employer?
b) *Rights of way or other easements*
   — Is there any indication of past usage of the site by others?

Boundaries

a) *Flank walls*
   — Is a schedule of condition required and will finishing treatment be required to the wall?
b) *Fencing*
   — What is the condition of the existing fencing and what new fences will be required when the site is developed?

Trees

a) *On the site to be cleared*
   — Are they to be retained or protected?
   — Are any tree preservation orders in force?
b) *Near entrances to the site*
   — Are they undamaged?

Basements

a) *Underfloor basements*
   — Are they to be filled or left open?
b) *Coal cellars*
   — Do cellars under the pavement have to be filled with lean mix concrete?

Footpaths and access to site

a) *Paving*
   — What is the condition of the paving around the site?
b) *Access to site*
   — Will any special precautions have to be taken to protect the public and to ensure easy access for delivery vehicles?

Services and drainage

— Have appropriate service authorities been notified?
— Are service cables and pipes to be sealed off or diverted?

Photographs

— Will photographs be required if any of the points listed above are likely to be queried at a later date?

Special precautions which may affect clauses in the contract documents	a) *Noise* — Will restricted hours of working have to be kept to ensure that no complaints arise which may stop or delay the contract? b) *Dust* — Will special care, dust sheets and hosing be necessary? c) *Mud on road* — Before they leave the site will lorries need to be checked and to have their wheels hosed?
Street furniture	— Are telephone boxes, pillar boxes, etc., to remain in use throughout the contract and will protection or special access arrangements be required?
Road closures or diversions	— If these have to be arranged with the Local Authority this should be done as soon as possible to avoid delay on the Contract.

B) When contract work commences on site:

Nuisances	— Does the work in any way disturb owners of adjoining property or members of the public?
Planning	— Do the site and the demolition method appear tidy and well-organised?
Supervision	— Is the Supervisor in control of the work competent and is he. carrying out the Architect's instructions?

C) Before the site is accepted as complete:

Fencing	— Is the fencing satisfactory and the site secure?
Demolition	— Have all the concrete, brickwork foundations, old footings or other underground obstructions detailed to be removed under the terms of the Specification of Works been broken up and cleared from the site? — Has the site been levelled, and satisfactorily cleared? — Is there any sign of damage to adjoining properties, fencing or pavings?

ITEMS TO BE CHECKED BY THE SUPERVISOR

A) Before the work commences:

Site operatives	— Have all persons employed on the site been informed of the type of work being carried out, their part in the operation, and how they can best carry out their individual tasks safely and efficiently?
Previous use of premises	— Have enquiries been made into the past use of the premises? Could there be any danger from inflammable materials, toxic wastes, or radio active substances?
Fencing, shoring and scaffolding	— Check if required and arrange for erection if necessary.

B) When work commences on site:

Protective clothing	— Is protective clothing being worn? — Is safety equipment being used?
Fencing and scaffolding	— Is the site properly enclosed and is any protection required for passers-by?

Men on site	— Are all the men working on the project physically fit and competent?
Equipment and machinery	— Is all equipment in well-maintained working order?
Burning of rubbish on site	— Is all burning of rubbish or timber on the site being kept under constant supervision and control?
Pulling down by machinery	— Is all personnel being kept well clear when demolition ball, pusher arm, explosives, etc., are being used?
Dust	— Is sufficient watering being done to prevent dust circulating?

C) Before completing site works and leaving:

Fencing	— Is the site fenced and sufficiently clean and tidy?
Adjoining properties	— Is temporary weatherproofing completed on adjoining buildings?
Completion	— Has a final hand-over date on which the site will become the builder's responsibility been agreed upon and noted in writing?

Appendix 2

Typical Specification and Conditions of Contract

OUTLINE SPECIFICATION

Specification and Estimate of Works required to be done in the demolition of houses, factories, and other buildings at:—

(Insert address of properties to be demolished).

Scope of contract

The structure to be demolished comprises:—

(Insert at this point a brief description of the properties to be demolished, with approximate dimensions and reference to plans or drawings.).

Inspection of properties

Contractors are required to visit the site and to ascertain the nature and extent of the work involved, and arrangements to do so should be made with the Architect.

Fires on site

The disposal of materials and rubbish by burning on site will not be permitted under any circumstances whatever and no fires will be permitted on site.

Watchmen

A competent Watchman is to be appointed by the Contractor and will be required to be in attendance at weekends and during hours of darkness. The whole of the cost is to be included in the Contractor's tender.

Avoidance of nuisance and protection of members of the public and vehicular traffic

The demolition of the property is to be carried out in such a manner as to cause as little inconvenience to adjoining property owners and/or the public as possible, and the Contractor will be held responsible for any claim which may arise from disregard of this clause.

A close boarded hoarding at least 8 feet high and of construction to be approved by the Architect is to be erected along the front of the property being demolished and removed at completion, and the Contractor will include the cost of these hoardings in his tender.

Fans of adequate close boarded construction are to be extended from the first floor of the property being demolished. All roof coverings and timbers are to be removed prior to the pulling down of the building. Notices of adequate size and construction are to be placed to warn passers-by of any danger.

Mud from the site

Before leaving the site, all vehicles are to be hosed down and all mud removed from the tyres, and the Contractor will be responsible for ensuring that the surfaces of adjoining roads remain clean at all times during the carrying out of the Contract.

Foreman

The Contractor is to allow in his tender for the cost of keeping a competent foreman-in-charge in attendance throughout the duration of the work.

Coins, antiquities, etc.

Any coins or antiquities found on the site are to become the property of the Employer and are to be handed over to the Architect.

Plant

The Contractor is to provide all requisite plant, scaffolding and hoists and any cartage, workmanship and materials which, although not specifically mentioned, may be necessary for the proper completion of the work described herein.

Water

The Contractor is to pay all charges for water required for the works, and supply all tanks, temporary service pipes, stopcocks, temporary connections, etc.

Watching and lighting

The Contractor is to provide all watching and lighting required throughout the duration of the Contract.

Salvaged materials

Should the Architect decide that parts of any buildings are of historic interest or of particular use to the Employer, these parts shall be carefully dismantled and stored in a convenient area of the site for retention by the Employer, and if the Architect deems it to be reasonable an allowance will be made for the value thereof.

Protection of property, etc.

The Contractor shall take all necessary steps to protect adjoining property, fences, public highways, etc., and will be held responsible for any damage occurring thereto, however caused, and will be charged for their necessary repair. The Contractor shall provide and erect to the satisfaction of the Architect all necessary protective screens or scaffolds that may be required, of a sufficiently substantial nature to prevent damage, nuisance or disturbance by debris or dust to adjoining properties, public highways or persons or traffic passing nearby.

During the demolition works no wall or part of the structure shall be left in a dangerous or insecure condition at any time when a representative of the Contractor is not on the site, and adequate barriers and (after darkness) lamps shall be provided to warn users of the public highway of any obstruction or danger.

The Contractor shall bear in mind that demolition sites are of special attraction to children and shall take all reasonable precautions to warn children of the danger of trespassing and to deter them from so doing. The Contractor must keep all public footpaths adjoining the sites available at all times for use by the public, and the stacking of timber and other materials thereon is expressly forbidden.

No mechanical plant or vehicles shall be permitted to cross a paved public footway unless there is a permanent footway crossing in existence or a temporary footway crossing has been constructed. One such temporary footway crossing of sufficient width shall normally be permitted at each site. The footway crossing shall be the only point at which mechanical plant or vehicles shall enter the site.

Electricity, gas, telephone and water supplies

The Contractor must give notice to the Electricity Board, the Telephone Manager, the Gas Board and the Water Supplies to remove meters and services and to stop supplies at the point of entry to sites, and must also allow for taking down fuses, switchboards and carcassing and clearing away.

Temporary roads

The Contractor shall provide any necessary temporary roads and clear them away at completion of the works.

Pulling down old buildings
The Contractor shall pull down the whole of the existing buildings to ground level. *(Insert here the depth of footings or foundations or thickness of concrete slabs to be broken up.)* Basements, cellars, inspection pits and the like are to be cleared of rubbish and left open without any filling whatsoever.

Old materials
All old materials arising from the demolition are to become the Contractor's property, and together with all rubbish and debris are to be basketed out if necessary and removed from the site.

Nuisance from dust and mud
The Contractor is to arrange with the Water Board for the provision of temporary standpipes near the area being cleared and is to pay all charges for temporary water supplies and hoses.

Loads of hardcore and rubbish are to be sprayed with water to keep down dust, and each loading or pulling down operation is to be sprayed continuously. No mud is to be deposited on the roads in the area by lorries or plant leaving the site. The Contractor will be responsible for any complaints arising from this Clause and checks will be made to see that these instructions are carried out.

Old fences and hedges
The Contractor is to pull down all old fences and boundary and garden walls on the demolition site, which are specified by the Architect.

The Contractor shall cut down all hedges and grub up roots.

Care is to be taken to avoid causing damage to the fences and hedges of the adjoining properties and the Contractor will be held responsible for any damage, which must be made good at his own expense.

Timber affected by dry rot, and other rubbish
The Contractor shall take all timber out of houses affected by dry rot, cart it away to a suitable site and burn it.

Noise control
The Contractor must ensure that noise from the work is kept to the lowest level practicable, and without prejudice to the generality of this requirement he shall:—

a) site noisy tools, plant, engines and equipment as far as possible from the adjoining roads and buildings;

b) fit and use efficient silencing devices on all tools, plant, engines and equipment (although the use of acoustic screens and sheds is not necessary), in accordance with the recommendations contained in the Department of the Environment Advisory Leaflet No. 72 "Noise Control on Building Sites";

c) ensure that no engines or items of machinery are left running for long periods when not required to be used;

d) ensure that all entrances to sites are at points where the noise from vehicles entering or leaving the site will cause the least nuisance or disturbance.

Trees
No damage is to be caused to any tree in the area.

Welfare and safety measures
The Contractor is to provide and maintain welfare and safety measures and amenities up to a suitable standard in accordance with the Building (Safety, Health and Welfare) Regulations 1948, No. 1145, and the Construction (Lifting Operations) Regulations 1961, No. 1581. He is also, in

accordance with the Factories Act 1961, to provide the workmen with proper sanitary accommodation of a decent condition and to remove it on completion of the works. Whenever practicable WC's connected to a sewer are to be provided for the purpose; where this is not possible, chemical closets should be supplied.

Completion of work   On completion of demolition, the whole of the site as marked in red on Plan No.   *(insert here appropriate number)* is to be back-bladed, cleared of all timber, bricks, concrete and similar materials, and left clean and tidy to the satisfaction of the Architect.

CONDITIONS OF TENDER AND CONDITIONS OF CONTRACT

1. Tenders shall be made on the form supplied by the Architect without any alteration thereto, and shall be for the execution of the Work and in accordance with the following Conditions of Contract and the Outline Specification which the Tenderer shall be deemed to have examined. There shall be attached to every Tender a complete and unaltered copy of these conditions.

2. The Tender shall include all charges and expenses of every kind which under the Conditions of Contract are to be borne by the Contractor.

3. On receiving notification that his Tender has been accepted, the Tenderer shall, whenever required by notice in writing, enter into a Contract Agreement.

4. The Architects do not bind themselves to accept the lowest or any Tender.

5. In the event of the sum which the Contractor(s) is/are prepared to credit to the Employer for the value of materials arising from the work exceeding the Tender for demolition work, the difference between these amounts will be required to be paid to the Employer before the commencement of the work.

6. Tenderers will be deemed to have inspected the site and to have acquainted themselves with its location and layout.

7. The Contractor shall not, without the written consent of the Architect, assign the Contract or sublet any portion of the Works, provided that such consent is not unreasonably withheld to the prejudice of the Contractor.

8. If the employer has reasonable grounds for believing that the requirements of any of the preceding paragraphs in these Conditions are not being observed, he or the Architect or anyone acting on his behalf shall be entitled to require proof of the rates of wages paid and the hours and conditions observed by the Contractor and sub-contractors in the execution of the Works.

9. Damage to persons and property
   a) The Contractor shall assume all liability in respect of and indemnify and keep indemnified the Employer against all actions, suits, arbitration or other proceedings, costs, claims, demands or expenses which may arise howsoever under the National Insurance Acts (Industrial Injuries Act 1946, Employers' Liability Acts, the Fatal Accidents Acts) either at Common Law or otherwise in respect of

any accident to any workman arising out of and in the course of his employment by the Contractor or in respect of any injury or damage occasioned to any person or person's property or goods in the execution of the Contract. The Employer shall give written notice to the Contractor of any such claim or proceedings as soon as is reasonably practicable after the same has/have come to his knowledge, or to the knowledge of his representative. The Employer may, without prejudice to any other method of recovery, deduct the amount of any damage, charges, costs, or expenses which he shall incur in respect of any such actions, suits, claims or demands from any monies due, or to become due, to the Contractor.

b) Without prejudice to his liability to indemnify the Employer under clause (a) hereof the Contractor shall, during the continuance of the Contract, effect and maintain in terms to be approved by the Employer, and shall cause any sub-contractor to effect and maintain, with a company of repute, insurance against all actions, suits, costs, claims, demands or expenses in respect of any injury or damage occasioned in the execution of the contract to any person, or the property, land, buildings or goods of any person, including injury or damage owing to fire and explosion, in a sum of not less than £100,000 or such higher figure as the Architect shall specify in writing, in respect of each and any one claim.

In contracts for work involving demolition vibration or the removal and/or weakening of support, the Contractor shall, before commencing work on the Contract, show the Employer the relevant policy or policies of insurance and the current renewal receipts.

c) The Contractor shall also during the continuance of the Contract effect and maintain in terms to be approved by the Employer, and shall cause any sub-contractor to effect and maintain, with a company of repute, insurance against all actions, suits, costs, claims and demands (excluding Third Party risks the requirements for which are set out in sub-clause (b) hereof) mentioned in or to be reasonably inferred from clause (a) hereof, and shall cause the interest of the Employer as principal to be noted on the policy or policies of insurance effected by the Contractor, or sub-contractors, herein.

d) The Contractor shall if requested exhibit, and shall if requested cause any sub-contractor to exhibit, to the Employer the policy or policies required to be effected under this clause and all current renewal receipts, and if the Contractor shall fail so to do the Architect may perform the obligations imposed upon the Contractor and any sub-contractor by sub-clauses (b) and (c) of the Condition and deduct the cost thereof from any monies due or becoming due to the Contractor or recover the sum of the balance thereof by action at his option.

10. If the Contractor fails to complete the Work within the period stated on the Quotation, or within any extended time fixed under Clause 13 of these Conditions, and the Architect certifies in writing that in his opinion the same ought reasonably to have been completed, the Contractor shall pay or allow to the Employer a sum calculated at the rate of per day per property as Liquidated and Ascertained

Damages for the period during which the said Work shall remain or have remained incomplete and the Employer may deduct such damages from any monies otherwise payable to the Contractor under this Contract.

11. If, in the opinion of the Architect, the Work is delayed
    i) by force majeure, or
    ii) by reason of any exceptionally inclement weather, or
    iii) by reason of civil commotion, local combination of workmen, strike or lockout affecting any of the trades employed in the Work, or
    iv) by delay on the part of other contractors or tradesmen engaged by the Employer in ultimating work not forming part of this Contract,

    then, in any such case, the Architect shall make fair and reasonable extension of time for completion of the Work. Upon the occurrence of any such event, the Contractor shall immediately give notice thereof in writing to the Architect, but he shall nevertheless constantly exert his best efforts to prevent delay and shall do all that may reasonably be required to proceed with the Works.

12. a) If the contractor defaults in any of the following respects:
    i) if without reasonable cause, he wholly suspends the Works before completion,
    ii) if he fails to proceed with the Work with reasonable diligence,
    iii) if he fails to comply with the provisions of the Specification of Works,

    and if he continues such default for fourteen days after a notice by registered post specifying the default has been given to him by the Architect, the Employer may, without prejudice to any other rights or remedies, thereupon by notice by registered post determine the employment of the Contractor under this Contract.

    b) If the Contractor becomes bankrupt or, in the case of a company, enters into either compulsory or voluntary liquidation, except for the purpose of reconstruction, the Employer may, without prejudice to any other rights or remedies, thereupon by notice by registered post determine the employment of the Contractor under this Contract.

    c) In either of the cases for which the two preceding sub-clauses provide, the following shall be the respective rights and duties of the Employer and Contractor, viz:—
    i) The Employer may employ and pay another contractor or other persons to carry out and complete the Works and he or they may enter upon the site and use all temporary buildings, plant, machinery, appliances, goods and materials thereon;
    ii) until after completion of the Works under this clause, the Employer shall not be bound by any other provision of the Contract to make any payments to the Contractor, but upon such completion as aforesaid and the verification within a

reasonable time of the accounts therefore the Architect shall
certify the amount of expenses properly incurred by the
Employer, and, if such amount, added to monies paid to the
Contractor before such determination, exceeds the total
amount which would have been payable on due completion
in accordance with this Contract, the difference shall be a
debt payable to the Employer by the Contractor and will be
deducted from the monetary bond referred to in Clause 15;
if the said amount added to the said monies be less than the
said total amount, the difference shall be a debt payable by
the Employer to the Contractor.

13. a) The Architect may, without vitiating the Contract, vary the Works
by increasing or decreasing the amount or omitting any portion
or by ordering such additional work as he may consider necessary
for the completion of the Work. The value of all such variations
shall be taken into account and the Contract price shall be varied
accordingly but no work shall be varied by the Contractor without
an order in writing from the Architect to this effect. The Contractor shall execute by daylight such additional Work as the Architect
may authorise in writing to be so executed.

b) The amount to be added to or deducted from the Contract price
in respect of any variations of the Works ordered by the Architect
shall be calculated at such rates or prices as shall be fixed by the
Architect. Daywork ordered or sanctioned in writing by the
Architect shall be paid for at the following rates, which shall
allow for all supervision, use of tools and establishment charges:—

i) in respect of labour — the prime cost plus extras,

ii) in respect of materials — the prime cost plus extras.

14. No payment to the Contractor shall be made until the work required
under the respective order to proceed has been completed.

15. The Contractor shall (as the Form of Tender provides) deposit with
the Architect the sum of *(insert appropriate sum)* for the due performance and fulfilment of the Contract, and no deviation from the Specification of Works ordered by the Architect or delay or extension of
time for the completion of the Works or any other cause shall operate
as a release or in anywise relieve the surety in law or otherwise.

16. The operation in connection with the Works shall be carried out
without any improper or unnecessary interference with the pedestrian
and vehicular traffic in roads and streets and the Contractor shall at
his own expense provide, fix and maintain during the progress of the
Works such temporary gangways and other works as the Architect may
consider necessary for the use of traffic and the safety of the public.

17. The actual number of hours worked per week shall be limited to 40
for all classes of labour and the arrangement for spreading these
hours over days of the week shall be subject to the approval of the
Architect. In very exceptional circumstances these hours may be
exceeded, with the prior approval in writing of the Architect, but
such increases shall be confined to particular jobs and processes that
it is essential to complete in order that the organisation of the work
as a whole does not suffer.

Appendix 3

Typical Site Fencing

The following general specification for temporary site fencing to be erected on completion of demolition and site clearance is intended to be studied in conjunction with the illustrations in Figs. 17 and 18, which show the type of hoarding that has been found to be most successful and economical in use, though, of course, the dimensions of such can vary.

Ground work

On completion of demolition, the site should be surrounded by a 2.43 metres (8') high fence constructed of timber. This can be secondhand timber recovered from the demolition works, provided that the Architect approves the condition of such timber.

Before beginning to erect the fencing the Contractor should clear a strip of ground at least one metre (3' 3") wide along the proposed line of the fence, making this the same height as the footpath outside the site or any other level specified.

Posts

Posts should have a cross-sectional area of not less than 100 sq. cm. (16 sq. ins.), they should be sunk into the ground to a depth of not less than 610 mm (2') and should extend to the full height of the fence. The intervals between them should not be less than 3.05 metres (10') and each post should be surrounded by a layer of concrete (1:2:6 mix) at least 150 mm (6") deep.

Spurs

Each post should be supplied with a raking spur of appropriate cross-section which should extend for 2.43 metres (8') from the top of the post and then be fixed to a 100 mm (4") x 75 mm (3") stake driven at least 1 metre (3' 3") into the ground. The spur should be fixed to both post and stake by three 150 mm (6") long nails.

Rails

The fence should have three cross-rails and each rail should be fixed to the posts by three 150 mm (6") long nails. The rails are to be positioned the upper one at no more than 300 mm (1') from the top of the post, and the lower one at not more than 300 mm (1') and not less than 150 mm (6") from the ground, measuring from the underside of the rail. The third rail should be fixed midway between the top and bottom rail. All joints in the rails are to be made at the posts.

Boarding

The boarding must be closely knit and at least 19 mm (¾") thick; at least every alternate board must extend the full height of the fence and no board must be less than 1.22 metres (4') in length. Each board should be

Figure 17   Standard fencing for building and demolition sites.

Boarding to be min. thickness 19mm
(¾″) and at least each alternate
board 2.435m (8′-0″) long. None
shorter than 1.217m (4′-0″) long

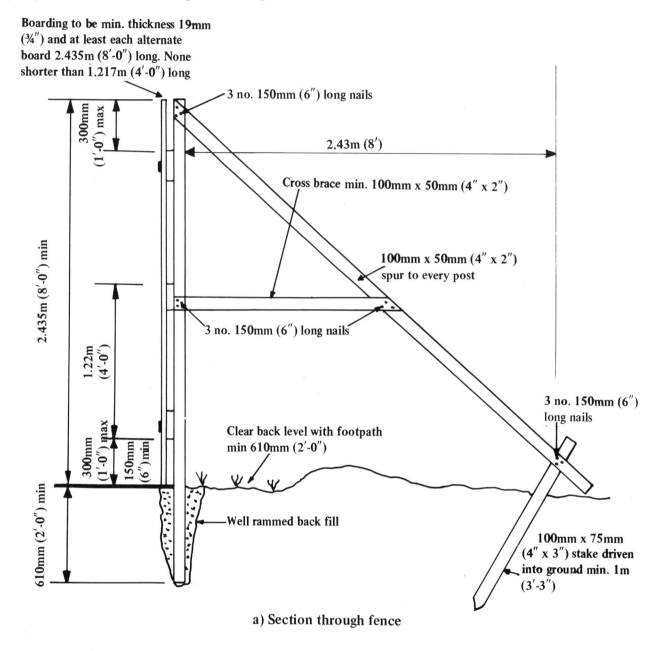

3 no. 150mm (6″) long nails

2.43m (8′)

Cross brace min. 100mm x 50mm (4″ x 2″)

100mm x 50mm (4″ x 2″)
spur to every post

300mm (1′-0″) max

2.435m (8′-0″) min

1.22m (4′-0″)

300mm (1′-0″) max

150mm (6″) min

3 no. 150mm (6″) long nails

3 no. 150mm (6″) long nails

Clear back level with footpath
min 610mm (2′-0″)

610mm (2′-0″) min

Well rammed back fill

100mm x 75mm
(4″ x 3″) stake driven
into ground min. 1m
(3′-3″)

a) Section through fence

86

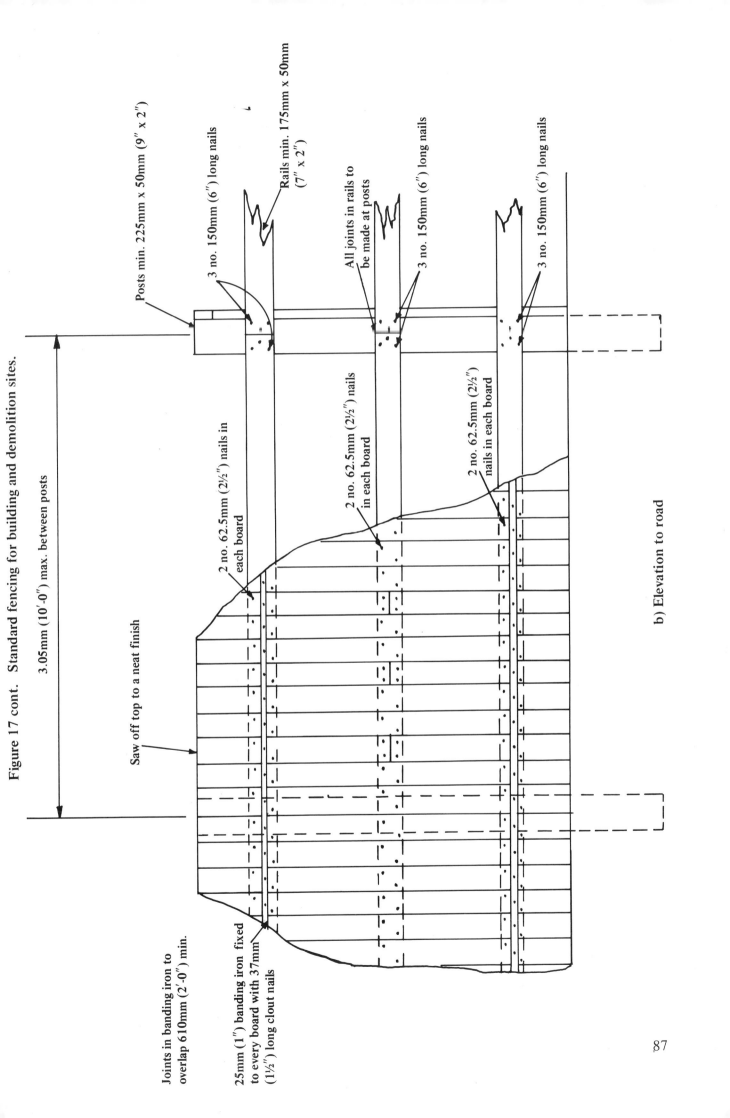

Figure 17 cont. Standard fencing for building and demolition sites.

Posts min. 225mm x 50mm (9" x 2")

3 no. 150mm (6") long nails

Rails min. 175mm x 50mm (7" x 2")

All joints in rails to be made at posts

3 no. 150mm (6") long nails

3 no. 150mm (6") long nails

3.05mm (10'-0") max. between posts

Saw off top to a neat finish

2 no. 62.5mm (2½") nails in each board

2 no. 62.5mm (2½") nails in each board

2 no. 62.5mm (2½") nails in each board

Joints in banding iron to overlap 610mm (2'-0") min.

25mm (1") banding iron fixed to every board with 37mm (1½") long clout nails

b) Elevation to road

87

Figure 18 A further example of standard fencing.

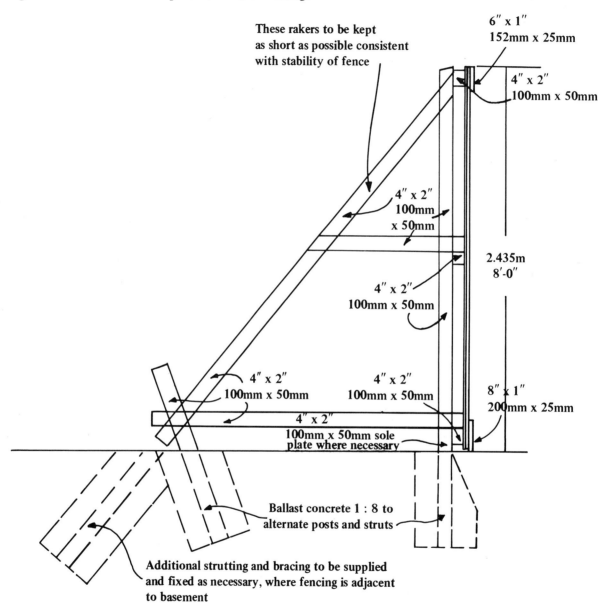

These rakers to be kept as short as possible consistent with stability of fence

6″ x 1″
152mm x 25mm

4″ x 2″
100mm x 50mm

4″ x 2″
100mm
x 50mm

4″ x 2″
100mm x 50mm

2.435m
8′-0″

4″ x 2″
100mm x 50mm

4″ x 2″
100mm x 50mm

8″ x 1″
200mm x 25mm

4″ x 2″
100mm x 50mm sole plate where necessary

Ballast concrete 1 : 8 to alternate posts and struts

Additional strutting and bracing to be supplied and fixed as necessary, where fencing is adjacent to basement

a) Section through fence

88

Figure 18 cont.   A further example of standard fencing.   b) Elevation to road

Observation panels required at 12m (40'-0") centres approx.

Hinge

152mm x 25mm
6'' x 1''

Hinge

Hinge

100mm x 50mm
4'' x 2''

100mm x 50mm
4'' x 2''

22.G galvanised corrugated
iron sheets

22.G galvanised corrugated
iron sheets

200mm x 25mm
8'' x 1''

Observation panel
covered with 75mm (3'')
mesh galvanised chain
link fencing and 75mm
x 25mm (3'' x 1'') wrot
slats evenly spaced
protected with two coats
of wood preservative

Hinge

4'' x 2''
100mm x 50mm

1.83m
6'-0''

Wicket gate

4'' x 2''
100mm x 50mm

0.914m
3'-0''

75mm x 50mm
3'' x 2''

1.83m
6'-0''

200mm x 25mm
8'' x 1''

4'' x 2''
100mm
x 50mm

1.22m
4'-0''

fixed to each rail by two 62.5 mm (2½″) nails. On completion of erection, the top of the boarding should be cut to a neat, even finish.

Banding

The fence should be strengthened by running 23 mm (1″) mild steel banding iron along the top and bottom rails all the length of the fence, fixing this to each board by a 1.37 mm (1½″) long clout nail. All joints in the banding must overlap by 610 mm (2′).

Gates

When traffic gates are required they should, unless otherwise stated, allow a clear opening of 4.42 metres (14′), be 2.43 metres (8′) high and have double leaves which swing into the site.

The gates should be constructed of three 152 mm (6″) x 50 mm (2″) timber rails with two 152 mm (6″) x 50 mm (2″) braces and should be closely covered with boards to match the fencing. Each gate leaf should be fixed to its respective side post by three 305 mm (1′) strap hinges, and the gates should be fitted with black japanned or galvanised hinged hasp and staple. Provision must be made on the site side of the gate for a drop board of 100 mm (4″) x 75 mm (3″), to extend 610 mm (2′) beyond the total width of the gate opening.

Maintenance

The Contractor will be required to return at short notice to carry out any repairs to or make good any defects in the fencing or gates for a period of three calendar months from the date of erection. The Architect may at his discretion allow payment at agreed rates if the damage is no fault of the Contractor.

Appendix 4

An Interesting Case History

"You can't live there — it's radioactive"

M. W. Pullin, B.Sc., M.INST.P., M.R.S.H. and P. E. Forrester, M.R.S.H.
Scientific Branch, Director General's Department, Greater London Council

The title of this paper was the headline which appeared in the press when a north London house contaminated with radioactive material was recently demolished. The house, a typical Victorian detached house of three floors, attic and basement, was found to be radioactive when it was taken over by the Greater London Council in preparation for the extension of a housing development.

In 1940 a small luminizing factory was set up in part of the house. The work carried out involved painting instrument dials and clock faces with luminous paint containing (originally) Radium 226 and later Promethium 147 and Tritium. This continued until 1964 when the factory was transferred to other premises, although the owner continued to use the house as his private residence.

From the enforcing date of the Radioactive Substances Act 1960, 1 December 1963 until the end of 1964 the company was registered under the Act to keep and use up to 25 curies of Tritium, 250 millicuries of Promethium 147 and 25 millicuries of Radium 226 and its decay products.

In 1968 the house, together with surrounding property, was purchased by the Greater London Council as the sites were intended for a future extension of an adjacent development area, but the former owner continued to occupy the house, as a tenant of the Council, until 1972 when it was vacated.

Surrounding empty properties had been offered to a local housing association for the temporary use of homeless families until the demolition of the houses was necessary. When the association requested the use of this house, the fact that it was contaminated with radioactive material was noted and the advice of the Greater London Council's Scientific Advisers' Radiological Protection Officers (R.P.O.) was requested.

The premises were visited and measurements were made of the radioactive contamination of the house and garden. The results of these measurements indicated that many parts of the property were grossly contaminated with radioactive materials emitting alpha, beta and gamma radiation and all other parts were contaminated to some extent, although accurate measurement of all but alpha emitting contamination was difficult due to the very high background levels.

Additional measurements made at a distance from the premises indicated that some tens of millicuries of Radium contaminated the site.

In view of this gross contamination by long lived radioactive material the Scientific Adviser recommended that the house should be demolished as soon as possible and the contaminated material disposed of safely; arrangements for this were started at once.

PLANS FOR DEMOLITION

Approval for the demolition and disposal was sought from the Department of the Environment in accordance with the Radioactive Substances Act 1960. Advice on the demolition was freely given by the Department and approval was given for the disposal of the most contaminated items to the Atomic Energy Authority's National Disposal Service (N.D.S.) and for the remainder of the contaminated material to the Council's refuse tip at New Years Green Lane, Harefield.

The public utilities were informed of the pending demolition and warned of the existence of the contamination. During the subsequent disconnection of gas, electricity, water and drainage, the R.P.O.s of the Scientific Branch were present to check that no contamination of public utility workers occurred. The Public Health and Borough Engineers Departments of the London Borough concerned were informed of the condition of the house as were the Metropolitan Police and the London Fire Brigade.

A demolition contract was drawn up using the contract for a previous demolition of radioactive premises as a guide. In addition to the normal demolition contract conditions, several additional conditions were inserted. Some of these were:

a) The Contractor is to retain the services of the National Radiological Protection Board (N.R.P.B.) to monitor and supervise the demolition.

b) The Contractor is to supply all protective clothing, respirators, washing and changing facilities including hot and cold showers as required.

c) The whole of the work is to be carried out in accordance with the requirements and to the satisfaction of the Department of the Environment and Radiochemical Inspectorate and H.M. Factory Inspectorate.

This contract was put out for tender by approved demolition contractors. Finally arrangements were made with the Council's Department of Public Health Engineering to receive the contaminated material at Harefield refuse tip, to bury this at the base of the filling face and to cover it at once with refuse and other inactive filling material, and also with the N.D.S. at Harwell to collect and dispose of the radioactive 'hot spots', items from the attic and cellar which were grossly contaminated.

The contract having been awarded, the contractors, N.R.P.B., G.L.C. Scientific Branch and Valuer's Department representatives met on site to work out the best method for the safe demolition of the building. It was decided that the 'hot spots' would be removed first by the N.R.P.B. officers and contractors' men and disposed of to the N.D.S.

The building would then be demolished by hand by the contractors to minimize any dust problem. The contractors were required by H.M. Factory Inspectorate to provide washing facilities including hot water, clean overalls and respirators for the men working on the site, who had to be registered radiation workers. Under the Factories Act 1961 the premises and demolition are subject to the Ionising Radiations (Unsealed Radioactive Substances) Regulations 1968 which are enforced by H.M. Factory Inspectorate. The statutory requirements of these regulations include:

(i) A competent person to be appointed to supervise the work.

(ii) Health register and radiation dose records to be kept.

(iii) Medical supervision of workers.

(iv) Protective clothing and apparatus to be used where necessary.

(v) No food, drink, snuff, tobacco or cosmetics to be used in the active area.

(vi) Person sustaining cut or break in skin must have it dealt with and monitored by authorized first aid officer.

(vii) Radiation Dosemeter or doserate meter to be provided for testing for contamination, etc.

Prior to and during the demolition several neighbouring residents informed the scientific staff that they were in possession of household articles from the house. Most of these items had been bought from or given by the previous owners but in some cases had been 'liberated' whilst the house had been standing empty, even though it was barricaded with galvanized sheeting at all ground floor windows. These items were checked for radioactivity and those contaminated were returned to the site for disposal. The items varied from brass drawer handles and carpets to an outhouse door which was in use in a neighbouring house as a tabletop.

DEMOLITION AND DISPOSAL

The demolition started as planned with the removal of the 'hot spots' and then the roof slates and timber were removed. Internal timber work was removed and the destruction of the brickwork was started.

The grossly contaminated items from the attic and basement, which were some pieces of glassware, drying shelves, ovens, a roll of linoleum and a storage chest, were sealed in P.V.C. bags and, where possible, contained in metal drums to prevent contamination. The drums and packages were then transported to Harwell for disposal by the N.D.S. In all six large drums and two packages were despatched to Harwell.

As the majority of the brickwork was inactive it was decided that a quicker method of demolition could be used and a J.C.B. excavator was brought in by the contractors, to demolish the remaining walls and to dig out the foundations and basement. The problem of dust was almost eliminated by the use of a copious water spray before and during the demolition operations.

As each part of the building was demolished, the rubble was loaded directly on to tipper lorries which were marked with the radioactivity warning notices required by the Radioactive Substances (Carriage by Road) Regulations 1970. Each load was monitored by the N.R.P.B. and an estimate made of the amount of activity in the load. Because of the high background radiation levels in the vicinity of the site the lorries had to be taken to another street about 100 yards away for the loads to be monitored.

A form indicating the type and activity of the load and emergency instructions was given to the driver for each trip, as is also required by the regulations. The lorry wheels and external surfaces were checked for contamination and washed down as necessary and the decontaminated lorries then proceeded to the Harefield tip where they were checked in and their loads buried. In all 95 lorry loads (approximately 950 m³) of active material were deposited at Harefield. As all lorries had to be emptied and their loads covered before the closure of the tip at 16.30 hours each day, the last load was permitted to leave the site at 15.00 hours.

As loaded lorries could not be left on the site overnight and could not leave the site in the morning until they had been checked by the N.R.P.B., the work of the contractors was rather restricted. However the job progressed slowly until the house was completely demolished and disposed of including the foundations and cellar, except for one cellar wall which was acting as a retaining wall for the earth supporting the house next door.

In the course of the demolition one of the contractors' men accidentally stood on a nail, which penetrated his boot and caused a wound in his foot. The wound was monitored for 'alpha' activity, bandaged and the man was then taken from the site to an area of lower background radiation level, where the wound was again monitored.

No measurable activity was detected in or near the wound. The man later went to the casualty department of St. Thomas Hospital where an X-ray revealed that a section of nail remained in the foot. The metal was removed and further contamination checks made, but no significant activity was detected.

Work was then started on the clearance of contaminated soil from the garden which was part grassed and contained several mature trees. Because of the general nature of the contamination the whole garden had to be excavated to a depth of about 0.5 m and removed. Unfortunately the earth around the base of the trees was also contaminated and they had to be grubbed up, cut into pieces and disposed of.

During one night, at this stage of the clearance, the J.C.B. excavator was severely damaged by fire and had to be replaced by a less efficient bulldozer type machine which slowed the progress of the work. The boundary walls of the site were then demolished where necessary, due to contamination or instability, and specialist contractors erected a sturdy fence to maintain the security of the site. A careful survey was then made and remaining contaminated areas were removed by excavator and by hand, and the site levelled except for the cellar excavation. As the cellar retaining wall did not look to be in good condition, the excavation was filled with inactive hard core from another demolition site. Another survey revealed a small active area in the region in front of the garage attached to the house. Careful excavation revealed a radioactive drain leading downwards towards the main house drain, which was excavated to the limit of the machine's capability and was still active, so arrangements were made to hire another J.C.B. excavator.

After a delay of two weeks until a suitable machine became available, excavation continued to the point at a depth of about 3 m, where this drain entered a larger drain. Here the radioactive contamination had fallen to an insignificant level. Excavation of the remaining deep drains on the site revealed no further sources of radioactive material, and so the excavations and drain inspection pits were filled in with hard core and the site levelled.

A final detailed check of the site indicated that the contamination had been reduced to a level that was not radiologically significant. The N.R.P.B. officers then checked the roadway in the immediate vicinity to ensure that activity had not spread from the site. The only significant contamination was found on stone sets in the gutter alongside the site and this appeared to have originated from the previous luminizing work. Where the activity could not be removed the sets were inverted as a precaution and the local borough was notified. These were subsequently disposed of at Harefield.

Thus demolition which would normally have cost a few hundred pounds was transformed, by the presence of a total of approximately 50 millicuries of Radium 226, into a large scale exercise in administration, planning and radiological decontamination. The total cost of this exercise cannot be calculated precisely but taking into account the contractors' bill, the time of officers of the public utilities, local borough councils, the N.R.P.B., the Department of the Environment, H.M. Factory Inspectorate, N.D.S., and the G.L.C., it probably amounts to several thousand pounds.

This report is intended to give an idea of the scale of the problems that a local authority can be confronted with when it acquires a property that has been contaminated with radioactive material. It does not include the pressures brought about due to the nature of the problem receiving wide publicity and the consequent, round the clock, requests for information from the media via the press officers. The possible general health hazards that could have occurred if the demolition had not been controlled are probably known to some readers, but by giving the extent of the problems involved it is hoped that any other local authorities confronted with such a demolition will find this experience of some use.

ACKNOWLEDGEMENTS

The Authors would like to thank the officers of the National Radiological Protection Board, the Department of the Environment, the Department of Employment, the Atomic Energy Authority and the London Borough concerned for their assistance.

They would also like to thank the G.L.C. officers in the various departments and particularly Mr. K.T. Smith of the Scientific Branch for his work on the site.

Appendix 5

Legislation and Publications Relevant to the Demolition Industry

Set out below is a list of Acts of Parliament and publications with which people involved with Demolition Contracts should be acquainted.

Anyone who is in charge of demolition should have studied:—

a) British Standard Code of Practice CP 94:1971, DEMOLITION, published by The British Standards Institution, 2 Park Street, London, W1A 2BS;

b) Department of Employment, Health and Safety at Work Booklet No. 6E, SAFETY IN CONSTRUCTION WORK — DEMOLITION, published by Her Majesty's Stationery Office.

The following Acts of Parliament are also applicable to certain aspects of demolition projects:—

Asbestos Regulations, 1969, S1. No. 690, 1969
Clean Air Act, 1956
Deposit of Poisonous Waste Act, 1972
Health and Safety at Work Act, 1974
Explosives Acts, 1875 and 1923
Factories Act, 1961
Construction Regulations, 1961 and 1966
Highways Acts, 1959 and 1971
Noise Abatement Act, 1960
Town and Country Planning Act, 1947
Water Act, 1945
Electricity (Factories Act) Regulations, 1908 and 1944
Public Health Acts, 1936 and 1961
Public Uitlities Street Works Act, 1950
Greater London Council (General Powers) Act, 1966
London Building Act (Amendment), 1939
Building (Scotland) Act, 1959
Building Operations (Scotland) Regulations, 1963.

Specific information is also provided by the following:—

a) The Quarries Explosives Regulations, 1959, Sl. 2259 (although these regulations are not strictly applicable to the Construction Industry, they contain general information on the use of explosives);

b) British Standard Code of Practice CP 97, Part 1, 1967, METAL SCAFFOLDING — COMMON SCAFFOLDS IN STEEL.

Index